MW00773369

DESSERT WITH BUDDHA

Roland Merullo

Dessert with Buddha
© Roland Merullo – 2022
PFP Publishing - PO Box 829 - Byfield, MA 01922
ISBN: 979-8-9866266-3-5
(also available in hardcover and eBook editions)

Front Cover photo:
© Ekaterina Goncharova / Getty Images

PUBLISHER'S CATALOGING-IN-PUBLICATION
(Provided by Cassidy Cataloguing Services, Inc.)
Names: Merullo, Roland, author.
Title: Dessert with Buddha / Roland Merullo.
Description: Byfield, MA: PFP Publishing, [2023] | Series: Breakfast with Buddha; [4]
Identifiers: ISBN: 979-8-9866266-3-5 (paperback) | 979-8-9866266-4-2 (hardcover) | 979-8-9866266-5-9 (ebook)
Subjects: LCSH: Buddhists--Fiction. | Spirituality--Fiction. | Self-actualization   (Psychology)--Fiction. | Atlantic   Coast   (U.S.)--Description and travel--Fiction. | LCGFT: Road fiction.
Classification: LCC: PS3563.E748 D47 2023 | DDC: 813/.6--dc23

MANUFACTURED IN THE UNITED STATES OF AMERICA

Praise for Roland Merullo's *Buddha* Series

"In *Breakfast with Buddha*, Merullo writes with grace and intelligence and knows that even in a novel of ideas, it's not the religion that matters, it's the relationship; it's not the concepts, but the people, and here are two intriguing men, one with his eye on the destination and his foot on the pedal, the other who knows that we travel farthest when we are still. You'll enjoy sitting in the back seat of the car as Otto drives on deep into the luminous heart of his childhood. It's a quiet, meditative, and ultimately joyous trip we're on. And it's quite a treat, indeed, to eavesdrop on these two inquisitive and witty gentlemen and hear what they talk about when they talk about life." **—Boston Globe**

"In this engaging follow-up novel, *Lunch with Buddha*, Merullo takes readers on a spiritual road trip through the American West offering readers a hero that's a bit jaded but loving; a little lost but searching. One can't help but root for Otto, despite—or perhaps because of—his curmudgeonly tendencies, and hope that he finds the inner peace that, even if he doesn't quite know it, he desperately seeks. ...A beautifully written and compelling story about a man's search for meaning that earnestly and accessibly tackles some well-trodden but universal questions. A quiet meditation on life, death, darkness and spirituality, sprinkled with humor, tenderness and stunning landscapes." **—*Kirkus*, starred review / Best of 2013**

"In *Dinner with Buddha*, Merullo masterfully depicts the struggles of practicing mindfulness moment by moment; Otto is not perfect and succumbs to self-defeating thoughts frequently, but it is his effort to learn and improve that serves as a powerful model. Merullo asks readers to be compassionate and conscious in a world of suffering, where following the road map of predictability does not give the best or even the most obvious answers. . . . Full of nuanced, thoughtful prose." **—*Publishers Weekly***

Other books by Roland Merullo

Fiction

Leaving Losapas

A Russian Requiem

Revere Beach Boulevard

In Revere, In Those Days

A Little Love Story

Golfing with God

Breakfast with Buddha

American Savior

Fidel's Last Days

The Talk-Funny Girl

Lunch with Buddha

Vatican Waltz

The Return

Dinner with Buddha

Rinpoche's Remarkable Ten-Week Weight Loss Clinic

The Delight of Being Ordinary

Once Night Falls

From These Broken Streets

A Harvest of Secrets

Non Fiction

Passion for Golf: In Pursuit of the Innermost Game

Revere Beach Elegy: A Memoir of Home & Beyond

The Italian Summer: Golf, Food, and Family at Lake Como

Demons of the Blank Page: 15 Obstacles That Keep You From Writing & How To Conquer Them

Taking the Kids to Italy

The Ten Commandments of Golf Etiquette: How to Make the Game More Enjoyable for Yourself and for Everyone Else on the Course

Moments of Grace & Beauty: Forty Stories of Kindness, Courage, and Generosity in a Troubled World

For Amanda

Life is this simple: we are living in a world that is absolutely transparent and the divine is shining through it all the time. This is not just a nice story or a fable, it is true.
—Thomas Merton.

I resolved to stop accumulating and begin the infinitely more serious and difficult work of wise distribution.
—Andrew Carnegie

One

I sold our house—the four-bedroom, gray-clapboard Cape where my late wife and I had lived together for thirty years and raised our two children—in the first week of March, 2022. The headlines that week were filled with the Russian invasion of Ukraine, Putin's war, an undertaking so purely evil that every decent nation on earth condemned it. Like millions of others around the globe, I couldn't stop watching the TV reports and reading the stories online and in the newspapers. I couldn't help wishing that something, some miraculous intervention by the hand of fate or a merciful God, would put an end to the suffering, terror, and needless death.

Different as they were in scope, those two events—the selling of our home, and the invasion of a sovereign Ukraine—felt to me as though they were linked. Maybe that makes no sense. I'm obviously not saying that the pain I experienced at letting go of an enormous piece of our family history was in any way remotely equal to the dreadfulness of war; or that my suffering, if that's even the right word, was in any way remotely close to that of the Ukrainians. What linked the two was that both of them engendered in me a certain kind of resistance to the harsher realities of life, a not-so-subtle NO!, and heightened the sense of my own powerlessness against the forces of time and human evil.

That interior NO! was like a sour tide washing up against

what I'd thought was a solid, if recently-constructed, spiritual rampart. For more than fifteen years, my brother-in-law, the famous meditation master, Volya Rinpoche (VOHL-ya RINP-oh-shay), had been counseling me to say YES to things, to yield, to accept, to embrace a belief in forces larger than my own petty wants and preferences. To *surrender*. I thought I'd gotten fairly good at it. I'd recovered, more or less, from the crushing loss of my beloved wife, Jeannie. I'd gone on, kept living, kept trying, kept encouraging our children, Natasha and Anthony, to do the same. Time certainly didn't heal that wound, and I'm not sure it even softened the pain, but, after a long period of sulking and self-pity, I realized the futility of saying no to Jeannie's death. I came to see that my stubborn resistance changed nothing and led only to bitterness. Day by day, with Rinpoche's help, I began to rebuild a healthy interior life from the ashes of my bereavement.

I was doing fairly well at that, not interested in another relationship, but functioning. I spoke regularly with my children, mowed the lawn, raked the leaves, shoveled the snow. I played tennis and had drinks with friends. I made several trips to visit my sister and her husband, who were living on the family far—now a meditation retreat—in North Dakota, thousands of miles and a universe away from my home in suburban New York.

And then I realized it was time to sell the house. And then the face of evil was on the television every hour. And then the NO! that had been sleeping in the depths of my psyche was awakened. It circled in my thoughts, as impossible to ignore as an angry hornet caught in a screened-in porch on a summer afternoon.

Two

Fortunately, my only sibling (her name is Cecelia, but I've always called her Seese) is a kind and caring soul, if a bit daffy at times. And, fortunately, she's married to the afore-mentioned famous Tibetan-Siberian monk, Volya Rinpoche (Rinpoche or Rinp, we always call him). Although I tried to hide this buzzing NO! of resistance and self-pity, Seese and Rinp must have sensed that selling the house would be painful for me, and they decided to make the long trip from North Dakota to Bronxville for what they called "a good-bye visit."

It was, as I mentioned, the first week of March, 2022, and, while the Covid beast that had haunted the planet for two years had not been conquered, it did seem that the virus and its various mutations were loosening their death-grip on most of the country. With the exception of my magical brother-in-law, every adult in our family had contracted Covid before the vaccines were available, and, to different degrees, we'd all suffered. Seese had caught it from Shelsa, her teenage daughter, had gone into the hospital in Bismarck for eleven days and nearly died. I'd managed to nurse the illness at home, but had been laid low for two miserable weeks. My daughter and son, thirty-three and thirty respectively, both of them in good shape and healthy, had shrugged it off after a few days of what Anthony called 'logy-ness', lost their sense of smell for another week, then 'returned to normal activity', as the medical people put it.

Though what they'd returned to had been anything but normal.

My brother-in-law had, of course, been unaffected. I say 'of course' because, over the years of our acquaintance, I'd come to believe that he was not exactly an ordinary human being. A Siberian-born, sort-of Buddhist monk, with Tibetan lineage, a shaved head, the stocky, powerful build of an Olympic shot-putter, Rinpoche was ageless, occasionally maddening, always kind, consistently unpredictable, deeply goofy, and, for me, a gift from the universe.

His teachings had been especially valuable during the previous months, because I'd suffered from the repercussions of a cardiac ablation—two bouts of pericarditis—at the same time as I was wrestling with the decision to put my house on the market. The house where Jeannie and I had lived for thirty years, and where I'd watched her take her last breath. The house where we'd hoped to live together into old age. Needless to say, it wasn't an easy decision. I was still fairly young—barely into my 60s—and had good friends in the neighborhood. Friends, memories, deep roots.

But the house is fairly large, and the emptiness of the place had begun to weigh on me. Eight solitary, post-ablation weeks recovering on the living room couch had put an exclamation point on that emptiness. The kids weren't coming back. And the snow-shoveling and lawn-mowing and shrub-trimming and window-washing, well, much as I like to keep physically active, it was getting to be too large a part of my life.

So, I cleaned up the place and listed it with Miriam Puncharowsky, an old friend of Jeannie's and a well-respected realtor in those parts. In the early weeks of 2022, the market in Manhattan's swanky northern suburbs was, she said, "hotter than Jacuzzi water, Otto!", and that proved to be an accurate assessment. One weekend of 'walkthroughs', by appointment only. An asking-price-plus-twenty-percent cash offer from a young power couple (Ukrainian Americans, as fate would have it) with a set of adorable, two-year-old twins. And the deed was done. Months earlier, pre-ablation, both my children had helped with the major clean-out, and said their good-byes. But Anthony was too busy at his North Carolina office to pay another visit. And Natasha, living in North Dakota and running the logistics of the meditation programs there, said she would be too sad. So, I signed the papers without them, put a few of the more beloved pieces of furniture in storage, left some for the new arrivals, gave the rest away, and embraced the memories on my own.

As soon as the purchase-and-sale agreement was signed, I fell into a mood slump (one of my many quirks is that I dislike the word 'depression' and try never to use it), so I was glad when my eccentric sister and her more-than-eccentric husband said they were coming for a visit. "We want to say good-bye to the house, Otto," Seese wrote. But I knew that wasn't the real reason.

Since Rinpoche considers air travel spiritually and environmentally harmful and generally avoids it, they rode the train from North Dakota, arriving forty-eight hours before the house was to be handed over. On my last full day there, Seese claimed, somewhat mysteriously, that Rinpoche "had an errand to do," and offered to take me to lunch at a favorite Manhattan restaurant.

The day was sunny and cold, typical of March in eastern New York. We walked to the Bronxville station, rode the commuter train to Grand Central, and strolled arm-in-arm to a six-table place on Ninth Avenue. The walk itself was healing. I loved Manhattan—that intricate, frenetic palette of humanity spread across twenty-two square miles—and had loved it from my first glimpse. The faces and bodies and languages and architecture, the crowded sidewalks and rusty fire escapes, the endless variety of eateries. Decades earlier, I'd arrived as a North Dakota farm boy, landed an entry-level job at a publishing house that specialized in books about food, and slowly worked my way up to Senior Editor. I'd enjoyed a solid career there, made good friends, had a satisfying work life. In the last few years, part of the job had entailed sampling the borough's array of ethnic restaurants—I'd had a regular column on them, in fact: "From the Streets of My City," in a regional magazine. A place called Kabul on Ninth had become one of my favorites. Seese and I found it unchanged. Matta, the Afghani owner, sat us at his only window table, tucked into an alcove two yards from the sidewalk. The three of us had a brief exchange about the war in Ukraine which, Matta said, "cuts with a big knife on an old scar for me."

He left to convey our orders to the chef, and we sat in silence for a minute or two, watching New Yorkers trudge past the window in their overcoats and winter boots.

"You're rich now," my sister said, at last.

I nodded, somewhat guiltily. Jeannie and I had never cared about having a lot of money. We'd lived modestly in Manhattan's Chelsea neighborhood at first, very modestly in fact, and then, year by year, money just seemed to accumulate. Two incomes, an exceedingly lucky house purchase, promotions. And all that in the era when the middle class had not yet started shrinking. We'd seen enough of America to know how high up we stood on the socio-economic ladder, and, at times, to wobble uncomfortably on that perch.

My sister had cared even less about money, and had lived even more modestly, at least until our parents were killed by a drunk driver and she and I realized that our plain old North Dakota farmland had become, in our absence, precious as sapphire. Seese had been beautiful in her youth—the object of many a farm boy's dreams—and had retained, even refined, her beauty into middle-age. Her blond hair was enlivened by streaks of gray, her wide-set, sea-green eyes edged with wrinkles, but she exuded an open-hearted energy that made her seem younger than her years. There was, and always had been, something both sexual and non-sexual about that energy, a way she had of seeming to be fully present, deeply secure, a little wild, and completely unguarded. It gave me great pleasure that, after a string of boyfriends that covered the spectrum from decidedly odd to truly bizarre, she'd finally found, in Volya Rinpoche, the kind of partner she deserved.

Seese had lived an unusual life—to put it kindly. For decades she'd scratched out a living reading palms and performing what she called 'past-life regressions' from a small, dilapidated bungalow half a mile from the center of Paterson, New Jersey. A flake, a nut, an empathetic but naive woman who'd lost touch with reality—that was the way I'd always thought of her . . . until she brought Rinpoche into my life. And then, too slowly perhaps, I'd softened that assessment and started to appreciate and admire her the way I should have been doing all our lives.

"Covid almost took you away," I said.

She offered her lovely smile, nodded, sipped the yogurt drink.

"Were you afraid?"

"Oh, no, Otto!"

"Really? Gasping for breath at first, then on a ventilator, knowing what you knew about the virus? And you weren't terrified? I had one bad night in the hospital after the ablation and I was shaken."

She tilted her head sideways and sent a puzzled look across the table. *All these years of meditation,* her expression seemed to say. *All that time with Rinpoche, and you still don't understand that death is merely a passage?!*

What she actually said was, "I haven't told this to anyone besides Rinpoche, Natasha, and Shelsa, but when I was really, really sick, when I really felt I might cross over into the other dimension, the strangest thing happened. I started to feel like my skin was a very thin barrier between me and, this, I don't know, this *air* around me that was filled with all kinds of spirits, and all of them were, I don't know, *rooting for me.* Like they knew it was hard, like I was finishing a marathon or something, and they were cheering me on. Rinpoche always says it, you know, but this was like proof that a world of love exists right there, waiting for us, surrounding us. It was so comforting. It was the opposite of being afraid. I feel like I can accept dying so much easier now. Mine, his, yours, everyone's."

Matta brought our food, a skewer of lamb with boiled, herbed potatoes for me, and lentil soup and lavash bread for my meat-averse sister.

"You're making that face like you don't believe me," she said, as she spread the napkin carefully on her lap, smoothing and patting it there as if it were a pet—exactly what she'd done since she was a five-year-old at Sunday dinner on the farm.

"No, sorry. I believe you. I've learned how unwise it is not to believe you when you talk about things like that. I'm just jealous, that's all. After the procedure, I told you, I developed pericarditis, the first of two bouts with it—big chest pain, impossible to take a deep breath. The first one lasted all night and it scared me a little. I would've been terrified if I'd been as sick as you."

"You wouldn't've been, Otto!"

I nodded skeptically, started to eat. The lamb had been marinated and spiced to perfection. Seese loved the soup and made humming noises after each spoonful. Matta stopped by. We showered him with compliments, and I could see that, even after all the years of rave reviews, in person and in print, the kind words still reached him. He'd found his purpose in life: giving people pleasure at his tables. And finding your purpose, as Rinpoche had written in several of his books, was one of the 'five pillars of happiness.'

When Matta left us to greet a family of arriving diners, Seese offered another in a long series of stunning remarks, the kind of surprise she'd been pummeling me with for most of my adult life. No prologue, no diplomatic softening of the edges. Only this: "Rinpoche and I want you to give away all the money you got from selling the house."

From long experience, I'd learned it was better not to over-react. "You do?" I said.

She nodded three times, energetically, and napkinned away a drop of soup from the tip of her chin. "You have plenty of other money, Otto. Your pension, the inheritance from Jeannie's family. Her life insurance. Your savings. Anthony's making a gigantic amount now, isn't he?"

"He is."

"And Natasha lives with us, so she's fine. Rinpoche is giving talks again, or he's had inquiries, at least, though I've had this really strong feeling lately that he's nearing the end of his speaking engagements, the end of that stage of things. His books sold like crazy when people were stuck at home."

"Not surprised."

Seese nodded. "How much did you get for the house?"

"After Miriam's commission and taxes and so on, a little

under a million dollars."

Another gleaming smile lit my sister's face. "And you don't need it, right? You're going to come live with us, aren't you? At the farm?"

"Yes, thanks. Only not in winter."

She laughed. "You can travel in the winter if you want. But otherwise, you have plenty of money and no place to spend it, right?"

"I have too much money, yes, agreed, if there is such a thing."

"There is, there is!" she said happily, confidently, lovingly. "You have to give it away! You have to, my darling brother, to balance out all the selfishness in our country and in the world. Maybe set aside some for Tasha in case she wants a house of her own one day. And give away the rest! So many people need it."

"I . . . we . . . Jeannie and I were pretty generous with our charitable giving over the years. I've already written some big checks from the house money. HBCUs, Native American Heritage Foundation, food banks, the Perkins School for the Blind up in Boston, a fund for Ukrainian refugees that a friend of ours started the day the war began."

"I know. You've always been great that way, you and Jeannie. But I'm not talking about only writing checks to organizations or schools or like that. I'm talking about handing money to people. Quietly, in person. Changing their lives, like, in a second. You can do that now!"

"Not following," I said.

She frowned as if I should have been following, or as if I should have been leading, should have come up with the idea myself, before she thought of it, whatever the idea was. "When we were on the train, Rinpoche mentioned a plan, and it clicked with me right away. I'm pretty sure I'd had a dream about it a few weeks earlier. He has to make a trip to Boston to see a special friend, and then he has a possible speaking invitation somewhere in North or South Carolina or Virginia, I don't remember. Shelsa said she wants to join him at some point. I'm trying to arrange a couple of other things along the route. He said the two of you should take another one of your road trips. You could drive there—it's not that far—and, as you go, just give money to people who need it!"

"Carry a big wad."

"Exactly, Otto! The country needs something like that—there's too much greed, don't you agree? Too big a distance between the haves and have-nots. Think of what great karma it will be!"

I did agree, and I did consider the karmic aspect. For years I'd been troubled by our national cardinal sin: people making a hundred million a year for shuffling money around or throwing a ball, while kids went hungry and too many adult Americans lived in poverty. In the second half of my life, I'd done a fair amount of volunteer work, tutoring mainly, helping young people from poor families learn to read and write well so they'd have a better chance in the job market. In the course of that tutoring I'd spent time in some of the City's rougher neighborhoods, and in doing so I'd come to see how easy it was, even in a jumble of a place like New York, to fall into your comfortable routine and avoid having to witness poverty up close. By accident, really, Jeannie and I had ended up in one of the wealthier suburbs, and it had given us a beautiful life: excellent public schools, safe streets, markets selling healthy food, families who raised their children the way we raised ours—to be considerate citizens. I saw how easy it was, how natural even, never to venture out of that luxurious bubble. Bronxville's restaurants, doctors' offices, shops, and tennis courts were all places we could get to on foot, or by making a short drive.

There was nothing wrong in living that way, nothing at all. Everyone in the country should have that kind of life.

But the truth was that everyone didn't have that kind of life, and it was so very easy never to look at what we used to call 'the have-nots', never to go into their city neighborhoods, or, in the countryside, never to venture down the dirt roads where they lived. And that made it easy, on some subtle level, to pretend those people didn't really suffer, couldn't really be hungry. Even seeing them on the news, even visiting for a couple of hours to tutor kids in a school or community center, one could still sleep comfortably at night, because hunger was invisible, and much of American poverty was hidden.

So, yes, we'd given generously to charity. And, yes, I'd done some tutoring. Once the kids were old enough, Jeannie—a museum photographer by trade—had volunteered countless hours at the local retirement home. Still, from time to time, a voice whispered that we were inadvertently part of a greater injustice, accepting something that shouldn't have been accepted: the vast gulf between the overfilled and the hungry, the spoiled and the struggling, in the wealthiest nation on earth.

During that conversation at the table-for-two on Ninth Avenue, it was as if my sister—who'd lived so much closer to the edge than I had, and for so many years—was peering into the place in me where that whispering voice periodically made its case. She was right: I didn't need more money. My children didn't need more money. I had—and have—no urge to drape us in the sticky cloak of guilt: we'd worked hard, lived good lives, been thoughtful citizens. But, once I'd learned what the house would sell for, I'd realized in a fresh way how wealthy we were. My children were already insulated—both by their education and by the money we'd set aside for them—from any risk of ever being hungry. There was absolutely nothing in the way of material goods I longed to have. I'd continue sampling good restaurants, yes, and indulge my love of travel. But—and I knew Jeannie would have agreed—I wanted to push myself over a certain, invisible line and into a level of generosity that made me slightly uncomfortable. I wanted to embrace the idea of *enough,* to live more simply, to take less for myself and give the rest away in what seemed to me the wisest and most humane manner. It hadn't really occurred to me to do that with cash, or as part of a road trip with my brother-in-law. That was Seese's idea, and, really, no surprise. I sometimes wondered if she'd been put on earth to push her brother out of his complacency in all kinds of different ways. She'd introduced me to Rinpoche. She'd tricked me into taking the first road trip with him. Since then, at every juncture, she'd encouraged me to step out of my upper-middle-class comfort zone and explore the interior territory that, she and Rinpoche both claimed, made the idea of leaving this life less frightening. Only a fool would have failed to listen.

On the train back to Bronxville—Seese had her eyes closed and was snoring quietly beside me—I looked out at the apartment buildings and bodega-lined streets of the Bronx and thought about possessions and money and the extremely temporary nature of both. I thought about my sister lying at the door of death, alone in a Bismarck hospital, about to be intubated, and feeling 'the opposite of fear.' I thought about the pregnant Ukrainian women being carried out of a maternity hospital the Russians had shelled, holding their bellies, as if their bloody hands and arms might protect the life within. It seemed to me then, as the train rocked and rattled into richer territory—forested hillsides, a golf course, a few large homes set back from clean streets in quaint villages—that Rinpoche had shown me a way to transcend the angst and fear and guilt and worry in myself. Like my bitterness and sorrow after Jeannie's death, that kind of mental activity helped no one, changed nothing. He'd shown me an elevated dry path out of that swamp, and lifted me back onto it whenever I slipped off into the muck.

It was less than a mile from the Bronxville train station to the house that would, in twenty-four hours, be the home of another lucky family. Seese and I walked up Hawthorne Road to Studio Lane, and there, a hundred and fifty yards straight in front of us, set up on a rise behind a neat stone wall and two dormant white dogwoods, stood the house in question. The place where the Ringlings used to live.

As we moved closer, walking not on the sidewalk, but right down the middle of the quiet street, I noticed a new-looking silver pickup in the driveway. It was parked next to my dependable old charcoal-colored Camry like the brighter of two siblings. "Maybe the Krasenkos are already bringing over their belongings," I said.

"Nope," Seese replied. "That's the truck Rinpoche just bought. A hybrid, he said he wanted, for the gas mileage. It's the one you'll be taking down south. I'll drive your car back to Dickinson, okay?"

Another stunning remark, another surprise delivered with her usual straightforwardness and innocence. "Sure, fine," I said, forgetting to ask if her husband and I were going to head south for a thousand miles, then turn around and drive all the way to North Dakota. I was too distracted. I was watching my bald-headed, maroon-robed, brown-skinned brother-in-law. He had a cloth or a towel in one hand and was wiping it across the brand-new pickup's headlights and grill, carefully, tenderly, almost as if he were polishing the soul of a loved one. When he heard our footsteps, Rinpoche looked up and immediately erupted in one of his infectious skeins of laughter.

"Otto, my brother-and-waw," he said joyfully, evidently pleased at his own purchase, and having difficulty, as he intermittently did, with the letter 'l'. He was positively beaming, giggling, chuckling. "They newed Rinpoche's driver's wi-sense!" he said, and the idea of that renewal—a terrifying idea, really, given the trouble he seemed to have with the rules of the road—sent him into even louder peals of laughter.

The beautiful sound echoed into the neighboring yards and against the front of the house where my family and I had once lived.

Three

One day later, we were ready to go. An effusive, two-minute embrace from my sister, with promises to see each other soon, perhaps at one of Rinpoche's talks, and then, after what passed for an argument between yours truly and my monastic traveling companion, he and I were settled on the gray leather seats of his new hybrid Ford-150, his worn satchel and my small rolling suitcase stowed on the bench seat behind us.

The argument—really just a brief exchange—had been about which one of us should drive. "Rinp," I said, "you had your license renewed, sure, great, that's wonderful. Congratulations. But you've done most of your driving in North Dakota, where there's one vehicle for every hundred miles of tar. This is New York, and we're headed for Boston, two of the worst places to drive in the entire U.S. It's a different experience, totally different. A mean-spirited circus on asphalt. I don't think you're ready for it."

"Ready, ready, Otto," he said, grasping the wheel in both hands and leaning forward so his chin was directly above the horn. Fortunately, the truck was an automatic—no clutch—but he was shifting his right foot back and forth from gas pedal to brake as if reminding himself which was on which side. We hadn't yet left the driveway.

"I'm telling you, Rinp, all respect, it's too risky. You need more city practice first. Boston is an especially hard place to drive. They're all nuts up there. Crazy, angry. All Red Sox fans and you have New York plates. If you get in a fender bender, you'll mark up your brand-new truck."

"Fender bender, what means?"

"A small accident. On a new truck like this the insurance costs will kill you."

He swiveled his head very slowly and held me in his coffee-brown gaze, and that was enough. I knew immediately that it was another of his 'wessons', that the conversation, however logical by ordinary American standards, had already revealed several things: that, even though I'd seen him drive fairly well on a previous trip, I wasn't trusting him; that, despite all the money I now had, I was worried about insurance costs—*his* insurance costs, not even my own; and that I was imagining in great detail a worst-case scenario that might never come to pass: Rinpoche ramming the back of some new Mercedes in slow traffic on I-95, the furious driver jumping out and screaming at us, perhaps holding a golf club, a baseball bat, a pistol. Other drivers cursing us as they went past. The police, the paperwork, the insurance entanglements, the potential for bare-knuckle UFC-like brawling in the Interstate breakdown lane.

None of that had happened yet and most likely would never happen. I sighed, looked away, nodded. Rinpoche started the vehicle and very, very slowly, backed into the street.

And off we went.

The road from Manhattan's northern suburbs to the capitol of Red Sox Nation takes you along various byways and then onto a notoriously busy stretch of Interstate 95. There are other routes, and perhaps we should have taken them, but it was a Sunday morning, I hoped the traffic would be somewhat more moderate than on a weekday, and it seemed wise to choose a road less narrow and winding than the Hutchinson and Merritt Parkways.

Rinpoche went along in the slow lane at exactly fifty-two miles per hour. Downshifting eighteen-wheelers, engines grumbling, pulled to within a few feet of his rear bumper. Cowboys and cowgirls, every species of road-warrior piloting everything from gleaming Maserati sedans to beat-up old Pontiacs, stayed behind us for two minutes, impatiently tailgating, then shifted out into the middle or left lane and sped on, sometimes offering the good monk a raised middle finger, sometimes not. Rinpoche noticed none of it. He was silent, focused, leaning forward, holding a steady speed and—not difficult to do at that pace—keeping a safe distance between us and the vehicle ahead.

I was white-knuckling, grinding my molars, alert for dangers, imagined and real. Without incident, we made it as far as the first rest area in Connecticut, and Rinpoche pulled over there for what he called "a breathing". We climbed out and walked the circumference of the parking lot for a few minutes. "You feeling not so worried now?" he asked.

"Yeah, but the hard part is still to come."

Another look. Rinpoche had told me, more than once, not to take everything he said and did as some kind of spiritual lesson, but there were times when I couldn't help myself. *The hard part is still to come* made me think of my own situation—a lonely shuffle toward old age, a difficult death perhaps, the final goodbye to the people I loved. When one reads about spiritual teachers, a lot of emphasis is put, not on their teachings *per se,* but on their presence. That was certainly the case with Volya Rinpoche. Being in his presence seemed to thrust me into a new level of awareness, a sometimes-fragile, alert-making mindset that turned ordinary comments like *the hard part is still to come,* coupled with one of his looks, into a bit of guidance. The hard part was still to come, on our driving trip, yes, and also in life. What was one supposed to do with that? His expression told me that one was supposed to take it as it came, not to festoon the moment with worries. To be there, to pay attention, to squeeze the sweet juice out of each hour without making everything sour with projection and fear.

"Okay, got it," I said.

He pinched his cheeks into a smile. "Good truck, yes? High bird." He swooped his hand through the air.

"Hybrid. Where'd you get it?"

"The truck place in New Roshelf. Nice man. Two times he went back and ask his boss to make the price not so big."

"That's a trick," I said. "They always do that."

Rinpoche ignored me. "Wery nice people," he said, and I tried to remember if once, ever in my life, I or anyone I knew had come out of a car dealership and said 'very nice people' or anything close to that. I thought of asking him what he'd eventually paid, after the salesman's two staged consultations, but what difference would it have made? If they'd overcharged my brother-in-law, he wouldn't care. He'd tell me that was *their* problem, *their* karma, not his. That he had plenty of money from his appearances and international book sales, and, on the quiet North Dakota farm, few expenses. That he'd made the men in the place happy by buying their truck. That the truck was the thing that mattered, his beautiful new truck, a high bird. What mattered was our great trip. Focusing on the duplicity in the world would serve only to spoil that.

I wondered sometimes how he would have survived, had he lived in New York City, where there were devious car salesmen equivalents everywhere you looked—apartment brokers with unmentioned 'fees' slipped in at the last minute, cabbies

that took you the long way to puff the meter, servers who added an extra bottle of wine to the tab and hoped you weren't so-
ber enough to notice. Another few seconds on this cynical line
of thinking and I realized that Rinpoche would have made out
just fine. People might cheat him; he wouldn't care. He'd focus
on the ones who didn't cheat. He'd 'lift up the mind' as he
sometimes put it.

We climbed back into the truck, and for the rest of the way
to the Boston suburbs I tried to practice the opposite of my
usual highway mind: giving more attention to the good drivers
than the bad. It put a small shine on the day, I have to admit.

Four

It wouldn't be precisely true to say that either my brother-in-law or I had mastered the use of Google Maps. He did not make much use of his old iPhone, and I'm not young enough to be fluent with modern technology, so it was a challenge to find directions to a place called Cafe Rossetti that could supposedly be found in the small city of Winthrop, in the shadow of Logan Airport, just north of Boston. It would turn out that, in order to reach Winthrop, coming as we did from the south and west, we were required to dip beneath Boston through a series of tunnels that were part of the famous Big Dig. If you haven't heard of the Big Dig, picture it as the almost-complete re-working of the circulatory system of an old body. Half the arteries and veins taken out, replaced by new ones. Tunnels dug, tiled, and lit, new roads curving here and there, rusty old bridges and elevated expressways taken down. A miracle, I suppose, given the scope of the project. And helpful, too, if, as we did, you had to go from the city's western suburbs to the airport or its North Shore. The new layout was puzzling to someone like me, however, who'd been to Boston scores of times before the Big Dig for book shows and pleasure, and thought he knew the city fairly well. Even the satellites seemed confused, if only briefly.

It was toward the latter end of the traditional American lunch hour by the time we found Cafe Rossetti—on a boulevard that ran along Winthrop's not particularly handsome strip of stony beach. We pulled to the curb there. We'd opened the doors and stepped out before I realized all the beeping noises indicated that the pickup, with its keyless starting system, had not been turned off. I explained the problem. Rinpoche laughed at himself, ducked back in and poked the button. The beautiful machine fell silent.

Rossetti's, more restaurant than cafe, occupied the first floor of a corner building and was furnished with seven tables squeezed close against each other and covered with neat white cloths. My understanding was that we were beginning our road trip there because of an important meeting with one of Rinpoche's numberless acquaintances, but Rinp had been coy about it, refusing to give me either a name or a description, saying only that this man was a very old soul, and famous around Boston. "Big man, Otto, wery big!!" he said. One of the two window tables had been saved for us. Our waitress—Vanessa was her name; I always ask—had the blunt, no-nonsense, city-friendly style I liked, called us "sweethearts" even though we were twice her age, handed out menus, snatched the *Reserved* sign from the table top, and sashayed back toward what I guessed was the kitchen. The whole place was so small you could have tossed a balled-up piece of paper from one end to the other with your non-dominant hand.

But the menu offered a cast of delectables. Various Italian-style appetizers, salads, pastas, seafood, chicken, sausages, and veal (which I do not eat). I'd been salivating over the options for two or three minutes when the front door opened and a giant stepped into the room. The giant—dark skin, gray hair to either side of a central bald patch, the strong facial features of a chieftain or emperor—embraced our waitress and the hostess, each of whom reached to about the height of his navel. The man must have been six-ten or eleven, and when he released the women from his embrace and turned to us, I recognized him immediately. I've been asked not to use his name, and I shall respect that request, but I can say that, on scores of occasions, in his green-and-white uniform, he'd broken the hearts of New York Knicks fans like me with his incredible skills on the basketball court. He was holding a bottle of red wine, and reached us in three strides. Rinpoche stood up and hugged him. I stood up and clasped his massive right hand, and we sat. Out of respect for his privacy here, I will call him Tom, but that is not his name or even part of his name.

"It's BYOB here," Tom said, placing a bottle of Barolo on the tablecloth, folding his hands peacefully in front of him, and meeting my eyes. "Mr. Otto Ringling. Rinpoche has told me so much about you. It's a real pleasure, encountering you in the flesh."

"I'd say the same back to you, but I've been a Knicks fan for thirty-five years and you caused me many miserable hours."

He smiled, a bit sheepishly, and I could tell right away that his sports career wasn't something he wanted to talk about. "Mind if I order?" he asked. "I eat here two or three times a week. And they have a special today I think you guys would like."

Neither Rinpoche nor I objected.

"Any allergies? Strong preferences?"

More headshaking. I noticed that Tom shared a certain *presence* with Rinpoche. They seemed to fill the room, and it didn't have much to do with bodily size. There was a sense of calm, of ease, of unselfconsciousness, which fostered the polar opposite of the feeling I'd had at some of the lunches with writers, magazine executives, and famous restaurateurs in the City. Those men and women had been trying to be large, and so had ended

23

up seeming rather small. Tom had the opposite *vibe* going, as my daughter Natasha would have put it.

He ordered, opened and poured the wine—which had a gorgeous dark plum color—and fixed his eyes on me again. An intensity there, yes, but it seemed wrapped in what I can only call *acceptance,* as if he were saying: 'A friend of Rinpoche is a friend of mine.'

"I've heard about your amazing idea," he said, and for a moment I must have looked puzzled because he added, "You know, the Giving Project. An incredible thing to do."

"Thanks," I said, trying to catch up. I hadn't realized our road trip had been given a name. Seese was behind that, I suspected. Tom was watching me, waiting for a better response. "I was raised on a farm in North Dakota," I said. "My wife and I moved to New York when we were in our twenties. We lived in Chelsea for a few years. Fifth-floor walkup. She got pregnant, we lucked into a nice house in Bronxville when it was still possible for a young couple without a huge down-payment to move there. And then, I don't know, neither of us ever really cared about money, but our savings just seemed to grow, and the value of the house went up something like a thousand percent over the thirty years we lived there."

"That's the way it works," Tom said. "For some people. Other people work like oxen their whole lives and end up with nothing."

"I know some of them. From home, and from a little volunteering I did in the City."

"I heard about that, another good thing. Don't you wish the so-called American Dream, that climb up the ladder, worked for everybody?"

"I do."

"Myself, I'm an extreme case. My family was the next thing up from dirt poor. Six kids, parents who never made any decent money and worked their hands to the bone, and, because of their skin color weren't allowed to get a loan for a house in a neighborhood where the value might increase. There wasn't ever much of a climb for them. No equity, no investments. No nothin'. But for me, their son, all different. I was twenty-two and had a million-dollar contract, benefits, endorsements, speaking invitations, and so on. All that just for being able to put a ball through a hoop."

"Do you ever feel guilty?"

Tom had his wine glass almost to his mouth, but at that question he went very quiet, eyeing me. He set the glass down. For a second I felt the way his opponents must have felt as he crashed his way toward the basket, ball in one hand, two hundred and forty pounds of muscle moving straight at them in great strides. "I've given guilt a lot of thought," he said after a second. "A *lot* of thought. I'm Buddhist, you know that, right?"

"I didn't."

"This guy here," a nod toward Rinpoche, "is to blame for that. I read his first book and *boom,* no going back. We believe in reincarnation. You're poor in one life, rich in another. Male in one life, female in another. Healthy in one life, sick in another. Straight in one life, gay in another, and so on. Changes everything, to think of the world that way. Makes it hard to hurt people. This is my rich life. I have a penthouse in town, I eat in places like this almost every day, four good kids, great wife, two beautiful cars, travel, the works. And I came, as I said, from a step above nothing. But I've decided that guilt doesn't accomplish shit in this world. Nothing good comes out of guilt. But I've also seen, in some of my fellow athletes and in some of the rich people I hang around with now, what you might call the opposite of guilt. I've seen how easy it is to get used to a certain lifestyle. Pretty soon the penthouse isn't so special; everybody you hang with has one. You get a beach house, a boat maybe. You vacation in the islands all winter. You don't drink ten-dollar bottles of wine, you go for stuff like this." He pointed a long, craggy finger at the Barolo. "It creeps up on you, year by year. Tailored Italian suits, the best doctors, every new gizmo money can buy. It took me about twenty years to get tired of it all, to stop wanting more. I still have the penthouse and the cars, but now I, we—my wife is with me in this—we give. That's our work now. We give."

Vanessa brought the first course, a caprese salad of fresh tomatoes and mozzarella, dribbled with Balsamic vinegar. Simple and perfect. Tom, I could already see, liked to talk.

"But it's more complicated than people think, you know, trying to be charitable. *How* do you give? What's the best way? Who needs the most help? Are you doing it just to make yourself feel better, out of some hero complex or something? Out of guilt? Out of idiot compassion, as the Buddhists call it? Is it better to be anonymous, or to set an example? That kind of shit."

"I'm just starting," I said. "Advice welcome."

"I don't give advice, Otto. I'm still figuring it out myself. But this guy here, this amazing man"—a swing of his wine glass toward Rinpoche, who'd been sitting silently and attentively the whole time, chewing a tomato now and saying nothing, "this guy offers one or two words, gives me one of his looks, and points me in the right direction. Right, Señor Rinpoche?"

Rinpoche watched him across the table for a moment, then hooked one hand up in the air above his head and said, "I want to learn to dink."

Tom's big laugh filled the room. "*Dunk*," he said, "*dunk,* not dink. You're not built for dunking, man."

"I want to learn."

"Can't help you with that." Tom's laugh was like a heavy stone thrown into a quiet lake: the big splash, and then ripples and chuckles easing out around it for another full minute. "You're something else, man," he said, beaming a big smile at the maroon-robed comedian to my right.

Rinpoche was smiling devilishly back at him. We finished the salad and wiped the plates clean with slices of soft Italian bread. Vanessa brought three large servings of rotini in red sauce with a single gorgeous fillet of halibut, small dishes of white beans to the side. We sectioned out the halibut and dug in. A young couple came through the door and occupied the other window table, glancing at Tom but seeming not to recognize him. It occurred to me how fleeting fame could be. A generation passed and, instead of being a hero, a god, a legend, you were just a tall black guy eating pasta and fish with friends.

We ate and drank for a while and Rinpoche and Tom caught up on each other's families, passing bits of information and commentary back and forth across the table. It was all very pleasant, but I could feel, in the same way I often did with my sister, that something, some surprise announcement, lurked there beneath the pleasantries, biding its time like a seed in hot soil, getting ready to burst into the light. When the dessert course arrived—three cubes of excellent tiramisu—Tom scraped the tines of his fork through the chocolate for a few seconds, then fixed his eyes on me again and the words poured out.

"The place I want you to see is just north of here, another small city, crowded, not rich, named for Paul Revere, you know, the British-Are-Coming guy. The amazing thing about this city is that *everybody* ended up coming, not just the British, everybody. First, naturally, you had the Native Americans. Revere has a three-mile sandy beach, nicer than this beach here across the street, and the native people used to have a kind of Olympics there. Games at low tide, races, and so on. Then, you know, the Pilgrim types, the English or whatever. Then the Irish. Then the Italians and the Jews and the Nova Scotians and some Eastern Europeans. Then, after what happened in Southeast Asia, in the seventies and eighties, you had a big Cambodian influx. Almost all the Jews had moved out by then. A lot of the Italians had moved out, to the richer, safer suburbs. In a little while, the Cambodians moved out, too, and now, well, you'll see, now you have Brazilians and Moroccans and Russians and Haitians and Nigerians and Turks and Guatemalans, and still some of the old families hanging around. Walk the boulevard, like I do a couple times a week, and you hear ten different languages in the space of half an hour. You see a bunch of guys doing their Muslim prayers in the covered pavilions, laying out their mats, bowing, and so on. Last summer I saw a group of eight or ten women and girls in full hijab going into the water up to their waists. In summer, you'll see a group of old Jews sitting in front of the bathhouse. A few guys speaking Italian. African American families. Dudes with their car doors open and Puerto Rican or Dominican flags flying and their music playing. Vietnamese, Turkish, Mexican, Salvadorean, you name it, you see it. And they all seem to get along fairly well."

"Soon there'll be Ukrainians," I said sadly.

Tom's face changed. The light in the room seemed to dim. "Isn't that about the worst thing you've ever seen?"

"Worst," Rinpoche said. "Wery bad."

"I can't turn off the TV," I said. "And I can't bear to leave it on."

Tom pushed a morsel of tiramisu around on his plate. "We can only do what we can do," he said. "In our little circle. We can't eliminate evil from the world."

"I know. Still."

"What you and Rinpoche are doing now, that's something, man. *That's* what you can do. If you're a good basketball player, play basketball. If you're a good person, then act out your goodness. That's the game. That's all there is." He paused a moment, lifted a forkful of tiramisu to his mouth, chewed, swallowed, looked up again. "I was telling you about Revere. I found the city by accident, but I've more or less adopted it as the place I want to try to do some good. My little circle, you know? It feels right, like touching the whole world. My wife and I—and we have a couple of people who work for us—we do our diligence. We find people who need help, all kinds of people, and who have a good attitude toward work and every-thing, and we've come up with what I think is a smart way to help them. I buy houses, mostly in the poorer sections a little ways inland from the beach, because housing prices in the rest of the city have gone sky-high. I don't *give* these people the houses, though, I *rent* them the houses. For small money. A few hundred bucks a month. It's better for them. They build up good credit. They get a feel for what it's like to have a landlord who isn't trying to screw them. They get in the habit of paying bills on time. If they stick with me for four years, I sell them the house for about half what they'd have to pay for it on the open market, and I co-sign the loans if they need me to. Now they own something. Now, maybe, what happened to you and your wife can happen to them: the money will build up, the eq-uity. They'll fix up the house, live there for a while, and, if they want to, they'll sell it and move someplace else. Or stay and make a life there, a few blocks from a pretty nice beach. Either way, they'll take a few steps up the ladder, and maybe help somebody else down the road."

"Sounds wonderful."

Tom smirked, gobbled a larger piece of tiramisu. "It is, it is. But now I'm trying to expand, to get a few dozen other people involved, which is where you come in. My tenants are longtime Americans and new immigrants, brown, black, white, Asian, all kinds of people, from here and from all around the world." He smiled. "I don't discriminate! We're going to visit one of them, a very special person, and I'm going to ask you to help her out, write her a check—your sister said you still use checks; we had a nice conversation, Cecelia and I. Write a check for whatever you think is a good amount. I already own the house, so it's not about that. It's about giving her a little breathing room so she isn't just scrambling to make the rent and buy food for her kids. So she can live *her* dream, not mine, not yours. Not what *we* think is right for her, but what she thinks is right for herself. She's a hard worker, single mom, widow—Assad and that other demon, Putin, killed her husband over there in Syria, starved him to death in prison after the Russians wiped out their neighborhood. So she's been through absolute hell, and a one-time chunk of cash from you can shift her into a whole other dimension. You up for it?"

"Absolutely," I said, riding a wave of his enthusiasm, maybe a little star-struck, and at the same time having zero idea what kind of money Tom was talking about. We finished the dessert and coffee and he insisted on picking up the check. On the way out, he leaned down and kissed Vanessa on top of her head, waved toward the kitchen and said, "Tell Stevie hi for me." And our unusual-looking trio was out in the salty air again.

Five

It was a fifteen-minute drive, north along the shoreline, from Cafe Rossetti to the section of Revere where Tom owned some of his houses. The Prince of the Parquet (as he'd been known by fans and sportscasters, in reference to the wooden floor the Celtics played on) drove a vintage black Corvette, and, with Rinpoche at the wheel of the pickup, we followed that beautiful car along a curving stretch of beach with a low cement wall and the ocean to our right, and a narrow strip of park, some boxy concrete condos, and a few fast-food places to our left. "Seems like a good man," I said.

Although there was very little traffic, Rinpoche was focusing intently on the road, gripping the wheel tightly in both hands, leaning forward. After a minute he said, "Good, good." But his tone made him sound atypically distracted. I thought it was just the new experience of driving, but then he added, "We starting something now, you and me."

"Right. The Giving Project."

He shook his head, "Bigger."

"Meaning what, Rinp?"

"New stage for you. In the spirchal. New stage for me, too."

I studied his strong profile—big neck, big shoulders, short arms. This was different. There had been times in the past when he'd talked about spiritual stages (*spirchal,* in his pronunciation), various interior obstacles for me to overcome, new dimensions to explore, the ego's subtle strategies. But the obsta-

31

cles and dimensions had always been part of *my* spiritual advancement. He always seemed to have reached a certain high ground and to be resting there, comfortably, assuredly, maybe permanently. Except for a few patches of gray stubble, he never seemed to age, to change, to have any place left to go, spiritually speaking. The idea that he was reaching a new stage; the idea, even, that there *was* a new stage for him to reach, probably shouldn't have been a surprise to me, but it was, and it made me suddenly uneasy. I was afraid to ask him to elaborate, and, as I sometimes did to stall for time, I pretended he hadn't said anything remarkable. I'm not proud of that.

We followed Tom's Corvette, left, away from the beach, turned right onto a busy road, and made a couple of zigzags into a neighborhood of small, close-set wooden houses, many of which seemed worn and low-to-the-ground. Roofs with shingles missing, bungalows with sagging storm doors, old vinyl siding, messy yards. True, it was late winter, a time of year when most northern yards look ragged, but this wasn't a neighborhood of nice Victorians on half acre lots. Here and there between the houses, I caught a glimpse of a broad salt marsh that stretched back away from the beach. We came to a railroad crossing, and a sign that read: NO HORN FOR TRAINS. I wasn't sure what that meant. We bumped over the raised tracks, made a right and a quick left on narrow streets, and then the Corvette pulled onto the sandy shoulder and stopped there, and Rinpoche parked the truck much, much too close to the pricey car's rear bumper.

The house nearest us greeted the road with two tiny patches of what must have been greenery in the warm months, one to either side of a cracked concrete walk, the dormant flora mostly weeds, with one small flowering bush tucked away against what was left of a picket fence. There was a sagging front porch, its white paint peeling, but the support posts were straight, solid, and new-looking. A back deck cantilevered out over the edge of the marsh, with another train track visible in the distance. The roof of the house looked recently shingled. As we stepped up onto the porch, the front door was opened by a five-foot-tall, middle-aged woman in a green head scarf. She had lovely dark eyes and there were small children clutching both her legs, boy on one side, girl on the other.

Tom had to bend himself practically in half in order to fit through the front door. He introduced us—the woman's name was Alinda—two more children, a few years older, appeared, and all of us ended up sitting in a small living room on mismatched chairs and a threadbare sofa. The family had clearly been expecting us. The older daughter, ten or eleven, carried in a tray with a teapot and cups on it, and her brother brought in another tray of cookies. Alinda was smiling at me as if I were going to single-handedly change her life and, at that moment, because of that gaze—grateful, almost worshipful—I began to have an understanding that what I now thought of as The Giving Project was going to be much more problematical than I'd first imagined. The kids were black-haired and lively, their faces bright, their eyes intelligent and curious. While their mother sat in a soft armchair, the older ones poured and served the tea and carried around the plate of cookies. The younger ones watched intently, shifting their big dark eyes. Tom was smiling, Rinpoche looked typically at peace. I squirmed.

"I am happy to have you in our house," Alinda said, addressing me, and speaking in accented, halting, but perfectly understandable English. I was wondering what Tom had told her about me, how the whole thing had been set up, what role my sister had played, and what, if anything, beyond giving money, I might be expected to do.

"I'm happy to be here," I said. Now Tom was watching me. Rinpoche was watching me. Alinda and the kids were watching me. I had a checkbook in the inside pocket of my leather jacket and was wondering how to take it out without seeming like the Great Savior. At the same time, I was trying to guess what range of gift Tom had in mind.

At last, he spoke up. "Alinda works at one of the hotels. We're not far from the airport here, and so all these new hotels have been built, and they need people to clean the rooms and so on. She's Syrian, as I told you. Lost her husband in the civil war. The family managed to get out, thanks to a local group in Boston, and she's applied for her green card, and the kids are in school and everything."

"Good, great," I said. And to Alinda, "I'm so sorry about your husband. I lost my wife a few years ago. I know how terrible it can be."

The smallest girl started to cry and buried her face in her mother's lap. Her brothers stared at me as if I'd come only to bring them more trouble, to remind the family of the horror they'd lived through. A few well-intended words, and the air in the room had gone from fresh to stale. *I know how terrible it can be.* In a sense, I did know, and it's never wise to compare suffering. But, awful as Jeannie's suffering was, she hadn't been starved to death in a Syrian prison, leaving behind a penniless spouse, a devastated neighborhood, and little kids.

We sipped the tea and took small bites of the food, the scent of awkwardness filling the room, as if the world's troubles, a sour marsh gas, were seeping in through the windows. I looked over at Rinpoche. He smiled, nodded, seemed to be encouraging me to say something else, but I felt I'd already put both feet in my mouth and so I remained silent. The whole notion of giving away money, the whole idea of making the trip, had suddenly lost its shine. It seemed there was a pressure growing in the room, and when it reached an almost intolerable point, Tom said, "Sorry to put you on the spot here, man. But you can really do whatever you want. We haven't mentioned numbers. The idea is to give her some breathing room. She's making her payments, working hard, walks both ways to the hotel, five miles round trip. The older kids mind the younger kids. What you give her could mean a babysitter, or a micro-wave, bus fare. She's not going to ask, she never asked me. *I* found *her*, not the other way around. But Rinpoche and your sister let me know you had some cash to give away, so, really, anything at all will be cool."

I pulled the checkbook from my pocket—"Nobody does checks these days, Pop!" Anthony had told me—and realized I didn't have a pen. Tom did. He handed it to the smaller boy, who carried it across to me. I set the cup on a side table and looked at Alinda, then at Rinpoche. Another encouraging nod. I thought about the house in which we'd raised our daughter and son, the multitude of bedrooms, the patio and yard, the three showers and expensive landscaping. I tried to imagine what the Syrian civil war had been like—the terror of bombs and torturers—what moving to a different country with four small children would be like, what losing a spouse, that way, and at that age, would be like. My thoughts whirled and tripped over each other. I felt myself starting to sweat. I looked down at the checkbook and took up the pen. "Make it out to you or to her?" I asked Tom.

"Her. Alinda Samaan." He spelled it out.

"Okay." I wrote that name on the line, signed my name be-low. Put in the date. Could not make myself meet Alinda's eyes, anyone's eyes. I had the pen poised over the checkbook and at last I just wrote in a number that came to me, which was actually about what we'd paid for our own home, all those years ago. I folded the check back along its top edge, tore it carefully from its untarnished brothers, and then stood up, crossed the room, and handed it over.

Alinda held it in both hands and stared at it for several seconds. Half a minute, it seemed like. She began to cry, big tears dropping down so that she had to lift the check away from the waterfall. She looked at me, at Tom, at Rinpoche. The kids crowded around, the older boy put his hand to his mouth, the older girl joined her mother in weeping.

I felt absolutely horrible, awash in confusion, wondering if I should have given three times as much, wondering why Rinpoche was doing this to me, what lesson was involved, because surely he'd known what would happen and what it would feel like. Alinda handed the check to Tom, who held it in one hand for a long moment, then looked up at me. "Good," he said. "You're a good man. You can't imagine what this is going to do for her and for these kids. She'll have to pay some taxes on this amount. I'll take care of that part, no worries."

"I am the nurse," Alinda said, rather suddenly, as if it were information she'd been withholding. "In Aleppo, I was the nurse in the best hospital, Al Mujtahid. I want to do that work again here." She paused and touched one index finger to the top of her forehead. "I forget the word for what I need."

"Certification," Tom said.

"Yes. Some classes. I need to make better my English, and to do the certification. My dream is to be the nurse here and to give my children to college. That is my dream."

"It's a beautiful dream," I said. "A good dream. We sent our kids to college. It can help."

I was babbling. To my right, Rinpoche was playing pattycake with the smaller girl, huge grins on both faces. It occurred to me that he hadn't gone to college, that my sister hadn't gone to college, and that they were two of the happiest people I knew. But I most likely wouldn't have gotten my job had I not graduated from college, so there was no lesson there, no absolute rule. The point, as Tom said, was to let Alinda have her own dream. The women she worked with probably hadn't gone to college either, and some of them were going to be stuck making strangers' beds and cleaning strangers' toilets in the Hampton Inn for the rest of their lives. No Corvettes and penthouses for them. No Bronxville four-bedrooms selling for absurd prices. I looked around and thought about the kids where I'd volunteered all those years, helping them read and write better, and then about my own kids, and then about the gray-haired giant in the room, and what he'd said about being rich in one life and poor in another. That idea seemed fair enough, if we did, in fact, live many lives. And it certainly was true that suffering wasn't limited to the world's poor: I'd seen what Jeannie had gone through in her final months. I'd witnessed the suffering—mental and physical—of enough well-off friends to know that money couldn't protect you from every species of agony.

I felt a little shift inside me then. The confusion remained—surely I might have given Alinda more money, and part of me wished I could have done it anonymously—but the point wasn't to try and eliminate all suffering from the earth. A spiritual conceit, Rinpoche would have called that. The point was to soften it here and there, to the extent that one could, and I was trying to make myself see the so-called Giving Project in that light. To work in my own small circle, as Tom put it.

That line of thought helped. It landed me somewhere between the self-satisfied savior and the guilty Midas. For the time being, at least, a more or less comfortable perch.

Roland Merullo

We thanked Alinda for the tea and cookies, stood up and shook hands all around. Outside, with the family watching from the porch, Tom enveloped Rinpoche and me in one huge embrace. "Good start," was all he said, and then he bent himself into his Corvette, tapped the horn, and drove off. I realized that I was leaning against the truck, drained. And at that moment, of course, Rinpoche said, "You drive now, Otto."

"I thought it was going to be simple," I said, once we were inside the truck. "I thought I was going to feel great. What I feel now is confused, a little glad, but pretty confused."

"Not about you, Otto," was all Rinpoche said, and I pushed the start button, holding onto those words, looking at them from various angles and trying to find the lens that would let me see my feelings clearly. It had seemed such a straightforward idea, giving money away to people who needed it more than I did. We still had a thousand miles to go, and plenty more to give away. Was it always going to feel like this, a weird kind of embarrassment mixed with a certain amount of pride, gratitude, and satisfaction? Was this why philanthropists donated through their foundations, rather than in person? *Not about me,* I kept telling myself. *Not about me.* Alinda and her family would benefit; that part was straightforward. But, somehow, that one visit had stirred up a hornets' nest of doubt, cast my thoughts out over the entire American landscape, all the need, greed, and ego, all the want, all my own pettiness and failings.

The hotel Seese had booked for us was a new Holiday Inn Express a few blocks inland from the south end of Revere Beach. Our room—spotless, two queen beds, tiled bath—looked out on what I would later learn was the former site of Suffolk Downs Raceway, a place where working people went to bet on horses in the hope they might suddenly become wealthy.

38

Six

Next morning, after our regular one-hour meditation, Rinpoche and I eschewed the hotel breakfast and walked a few blocks to Revere's Beachmont section, all low hills and old, close-set, wood frame houses, where, according to a friend who knew my tastes and knew the area, there was a genuine Italian bakery. Torretta's, it was called. We found it without trouble, a tile-and-mirror place on a corner, with the obligatory cappuccino machine, artery-choking cream-laden pastries, open shelves of bread and rolls, and—my choice for the morning repast—excellent biscotti. Rinp had become a coffee-drinker on one of our earlier trips, and a particular fan of cappuccino, and I knew he'd enjoy the biscotti. Though it was a cool morning, he said he wanted to sit outside at one of the small metal sidewalk tables, so I ordered, paid for, and carried out the food and drink.

On that morning I didn't want to talk about the moral and emotional complexities of charitable giving, and I was glad he didn't seem inclined to, either. "Shelsa having a troubles," he said, gnawing on the treat, breaking off a small piece between his back teeth and chewing thoughtfully.

"What kind of troubles? Seese didn't say anything about that."

Rinpoche took a swallow of his cappuccino, wiped the milk foam from his lips with a paper napkin, and looked across the

39

street at an elevated subway station where a train was making its loud arrival, all metal clatter and squealing brakes. He swung his eyes back to me. "People mad on her."

"For what? What she puts online? How can anyone be angry at a highly spiritual young woman writing about living a happier life?"

As soon as those words were out of my mouth, I realized the foolishness of the question. History was littered with people being angry at highly spiritual women and men, of all ages, who dared to give talks about living more happily. People didn't like to have their way of life challenged, and from what little I'd heard about my niece's words, challenge was the main thrust. Yes, her calls for change were aimed at making lives more fulfilling, and making the earth a kinder place, but no doubt some of her readers had their own ideas about those things and didn't appreciate suggestions from a teenager. I understood that. We lived the way we lived, and for many of us in the Western world it worked very well. And yet, somehow, we'd cultivated the ability to ignore the background to that pleasant picture—the high rates of addiction, poverty, hunger, suicide, and depression, the mass shootings, the environmental damage—and still think everything was basically okay. We clung to our comforts, many of them hard-earned. We ate and drank and partied and watched sports and painted window trim or paid someone else to paint it. Vast numbers of middle-class Americans went to school and found a job and started a family and bought a house, and if, as Tom had pointed out, they had a bit of luck, things usually got better for most of them as they aged, materially better at least. At least until they moved into the later years and that trellis of arranged pleasures began to fall apart.

Shelsa—Rinpoche and Seese's golden child, some kind of special incarnation as far as they were concerned—had published a blog and started giving online talks, like a Himalayan guru swept into the age of Google and Zoom. If my sister was to be believed, Shelsa had a sort of partner on the earth, an Italian-born boy seven years younger. A saint, the Christians would call him. We'd met him on our family trip to Italy, years earlier. In fact, that had turned out to be the purpose of the trip: to unite Shelsa with her spiritual 'partner'. I'll write more about that in a bit, but Seese had said more than once that there was a plan for Shelsa and this boy—Tomasso was his name—to tour together one day, a sort-of-Buddhist/ sort-of-Christian team roaming the earth with a small entourage, giving blessings and imparting wisdom. I'd been skeptical at first, and then, once I saw them together during our time in northern Italy, a little less skeptical. My sister gave me periodic reports. But it seemed that, even before Covid, the expected degree of spiritual fame hadn't materialized. The mother of the Italian boy had gotten death threats. The family was in hiding now, somewhere in the mountains of Europe. Shelsa, helped by her mom and favorite cousin—my daughter, Natasha—had made a few personal appearances before the lockdowns went into effect, but there had been a sense of disappointment, almost of failure. My own feeling was that she was still too young: Americans wanted their wisdom in a more mature form. Seese thought otherwise.

Rinpoche shrugged and seemed briefly pained. "How you call these?" he asked, following my example and dipping his biscotti into the coffee.

"Biscotti. It's Italian for 'biscuit.'"

"We had them over there?"

"We must have. You were so focused on the pizza and pasta, you might not have noticed. We met the pope! We met the Dalai Lama!! For once, food was secondary."

His face lit up again, all trace of worry vanished. The word *pasta* had done it, not any mention of the pope or Dalai Lama. On our remarkable trip to Italy we'd enjoyed a string of exquisite meals, and Rinpoche had formed a new obsession. Seese—who enjoyed cooking—told me he wanted her to prepare pasta three or four times a week when they were home in North Dakota. He asked for marinara or sage-and-butter sauce, pesto, spaghetti with clams. It was no easy task to find some of those items in the rural Upper Midwest.

"These are wery good," he said.

"You're becoming more of a food nut than I am. What happened to 'no attachment'?"

He laughed. "Not attached, just liking. What we having for lunch?"

"Jewish food."

From other trips and other explorations of America's culinary possibilities, I knew there was a famously authentic Jewish Deli on Interstate 84 in Connecticut, close to the route Rinpoche and I were taking to Manhattan. Rein's, the place was called. Here's how my mind works: From the minute I'd heard that our first two stops on our journey would be Boston and New York, I'd started thinking about Rein's, and what I would order there. Rinp, I worried, might have been infected by my passion for good food.

Or he might have been giving me another lesson.

"What's the trouble? For Shelsa, I mean."

"Tell you when we walk," he said. "We have to go put our feet in the water."

"Going to be chilly."

"Just the feet," he said.

On the short walk to Revere Beach, Rinpoche gave me the story of Shelsa's trouble. It was a confusing story, because some of it had to do with social media, and Rinpoche had never quite been able to grasp that part of American culture. He didn't know Facebook from Snapchat. He didn't have a Twitter account and didn't want one, though several had been opened in his name by various fans. He claimed to have no time for such things. "She wrote something for the Line," he said.

"On line?"

"Yes. On it. Some people made themselves upset about it."

"Do you know what she wrote?"

"About capitalism. That maybe is mostly good but might be some bad parts."

"Lots of people have said that."

"Yes, Otto. But maybe she said it a new way."

"Is there a better system?"

Rinpoche let that large question drift away on the sea breeze, unanswered. We sat on the beach's waist-high concrete wall and I took off my shoes and socks and Rinpoche unclasped and removed his sandals. I rolled up the bottoms of my chinos. He tucked up the skirts of his robe, and we made our way toward the water, stepping carefully. The tide was low, so we had to cross a fairly long stretch of hard sand, and as we went along, watching for the sharp edges of shells, I began to feel a sense of dread gathering around us. I had some idea of what Shelsa might have said, and in her wise, teenage certainty, how she might have said it. And I had an all-too-good idea of the kinds of things people might have posted on 'the Line' in return.

The water was frigid. Rinpoche didn't seem to notice. He waded in to his knees, letting the small waves splash up against the cloth of his robe, broad smile on his face. "We go to see a new part of the big country now," he said, chuckling at the thought, and then saying, "The South!" as if the South were heaven's finest precinct. "You and me, Otto." He bent at the waist and splashed sea water almost violently, a dozen times, up against his face, and so I did the same, flinching at the cold, not caring about the wet clothes. It was nice, a gesture of freedom, like we were little kids again and responsible only for the moment, not worrying about the practicalities of riding to New York with salty wet clothes, not caring what someone walking on the beach might think, not owing the world any particular kind of behavior. Being in the ocean had always cast my mind out to wider places, and that day was no exception. *Baptism* was the right word for it, but into what religion? The religion Rinpoche had introduced me to, I suppose, the religion of the open mind, the open heart, not Buddhism exactly, not Zen, not Judaism, not Islam or Christianity, but a way of being fully alive, present, caring, giving, spontaneous, radically sane. Shelsa had been born with that spirit and raised in it by this odd monk and my even odder sister. Was it any wonder she was having problems with the Twitterverse?

Seven

With Rinpoche at the wheel, we made the slow drive beneath the city and out through Boston's western suburbs. By then, the day had turned plain and dreary, pocked with quick rain showers and a few wet flakes of snow, the kind of weather that made me glad we were headed to warmer territory. No longer a skier, never a snowmobiler, I'd lost my patience with northern winters and hoped never to experience one again; never have to scrape ice from my windshield; never have to worry about slipping on the frozen back steps some night and lying there half-conscious in the darkness, slowly freezing to death; never have to miss months of outdoor tennis and weeks of sunlight.

Though I do enjoy shoveling snow.

Around Boston, New York, and Philadelphia—the northeastern cities I knew best—it was always surprising to me how quickly the densely populated centers gave way to suburbs, and the suburbs to countryside. On the outskirts of Bismarck, of course, the big city of my youth, that transition was so much more rapid: twenty minutes from East Main Avenue you were in rangeland and farmland, great stretches of both. Flying over the country, as I did on my trips to the farm, or as I had done for book conferences in California and other places, you had a sense of how massive America was, so much of it empty of human habitation. It certainly seemed to be true that landscape

45

influenced politics. Even Massachusetts, from what I under-stood, went from more liberal to more conservative as you headed west from Greater Boston. I wondered, given the great rift in my great nation, if rather than taking a term abroad, as Natasha had thought of doing—or in addition to such pro-grams—we should arrange for college students to spend time in the countryside if they're city kids, or in the city if, like me, they're born and raised in the outback. That was just more use-less musing, I suppose, but the divisiveness in our society trou-bled me. On certain days I even thought I sensed the rancid smell of a bitter secession, or another civil war.

At that time of year the forested hills of central Massachu-setts had lost all their color, trading the deep greens of summer and what I remembered as the spectacular scarlets and golds of fall, for early March's plain browns and grays, wet leafless branches, a few small patches of snow in the shadowed dells. I'd made that drive at least a dozen times, but on that day, un-der those gray skies, it seemed to me that we were passing through a landscape of nothingness, and I felt a low cloud set-tle over my interior world. At one point, a few miles west of Worcester ("Wuhstah" is how they pronounce it there, I be-lieve), I switched on the radio and, after ten minutes of the ab-solute horror in Ukraine (Putin, with his assault on Kyiv failing, had resorted to shelling civilian targets) caught a story of linger-ing Covid pockets in places where Americans had refused the vaccine. Then there was the report of yet another recount of ballots that had already been cast, counted, and certified more than a year earlier. Supply-chain troubles, the threat of inflation. Next item: another mass shooting, this one in Louisiana—four dead. The segment finished with a description of temperatures in Colorado so unseasonably warm that the ski season looked to be ending prematurely.

I had friends for whom these broadcasts—day after day, radio, TV, online—resulted in a persistent, low-grade depression. Choice of medications, side-effects of those medications, and selection of therapists, were regular subjects of our lunch conversations. Bad enough, those friends said, that we'd endured the terrors and deprivations of the pandemic; now we'd emerged into a nation torn in half, a new American world in which the usual pleasures were suspect and unreliable, and the threat of nuclear war had again arisen. There were even some Americans, a few of them famous, who appeared almost to be taking Putin's side.

The news seemed designed to make us feel guilty, terrified, hopeless, or all of the above. I confronted the same shadows, of course. On certain nights, even before the outbreak of war in Ukraine, alone in the big Bronxville house, with my wife gone, career over, and children far away, I'd felt as though something were seeping out of the walls, some bad spirit uttering the words of a radio broadcast, portending a dark new chapter of history.

But, over the years of our acquaintance, my brother-in-law had given me an antidote to all that. He'd introduced me to meditation, patiently guided me through a disciplined practice, and, while those quiet hours hadn't resulted in any mystical visions, hadn't cured the usual aches and strains of advancing age, hadn't changed the actual societal ills by even the smallest bit, they *had* given me a measure of contentment. I did what little I could to make things better, but in the midst of that, I was able to look at my thoughts and see them as just that—thoughts—and most of the time I could shift my attention out of myself and my worries and woes and toward the firm realities of the moment. More than that, the practice had given me a concrete sense of the temporariness of everything, as if the struggles of the day were set against the sweep of eternity, as if there might be a promise of some other dimension of life, somehow, somewhere, when all this was over. I switched off the radio and focused on what I could see: a hawk fleeing to a high branch, the rusty undercarriage of a tractor-trailer with Saskatchewan plates, Rinpoche's hands on the wheel, the thin frosting of gray-brown stubble on his cheeks. *Let it go,* I told myself. *In this moment, there's nothing you can do to change the world and ease the suffering. Let it go.*

Rinpoche seemed to be handling the driving pretty well, edging the pickup toward the low sixties, so I felt comfortable risking a question.

"Rinp," I said, testing the concentration waters.

He waited a few seconds and said, "Otto."

"I feel lately like I'm entering a new stage of life. Inside, I mean. Selling the house was like a concrete, outer manifestation of that, but I've been feeling it for a while. Almost as if I've turned the final corner on a race track and I'm heading for the finish line. And I'm wondering what, exactly, I should do from here on in. Hug the rail, take an outside lane. Crack the whip. What's the right strategy?"

Without moving his eyes from the road he said, "You talkin' funny."

"Horse racing imagery. You're the metaphor guy."

The good monk shook his head, puzzled.

"From here to the end, what do I do with my life? I mean, part of it I know: eat, sleep, meditate, be generous, spend time with you and Seese and Tasha and Shelsa at the farm. But I mean *interiorly.* I feel like something's there, some task, some route I should take. I have friends my age who've gotten more bitter, cynical, and afraid with every passing year, and I don't want that. They can't do some of the stuff they used to do, and they have all kinds of new medical problems. If they eat what they want to eat, they gain weight. Their sex lives are diminished or done with. Their kids are gone. Their work is finished. The country looks to them like it's rotting away. The world looks like hell. Please advise."

A small smile, a quick shift of the eyes. No answer.

I waited a bit, then said, "In a minute here you're going to take I-84 toward New York. Just stay in this lane. You'll see it."

Rinpoche held to a calm silence for the last mile, then took the exit and looped around in a large circle onto I-84. Most of the cars had New York and New Jersey plates now, the traffic moved a little faster, felt a little wilder, as if the I-90/I-84 fork had shunted the mellower types off toward the Berkshires and Saskatchewan, and siphoned the road warriors onto the southern route. After a minute, Rinpoche said, "I watch the horse runnings a few times, Otto. With my friend, Les. At home."

Seese had told me about her husband's friendship with a neighboring North Dakota farmer, Lesley Ingler. Rinpoche, she said, would go over to Les's place on weekend afternoons and winter evenings, play cards and listen to him talk about farming and Jesus, and spout various theories having to do with a possible Chinese invasion and secret government plans to turn American children into robots. The Inglers had lived on that property for five generations and, even in my youth, had floated along in a strange orbit on the outskirts of Dickinson society, sometimes placing handmade signs around the edges of their 3,000 acre soybean farm with messages like these: *LIE-BERRIE'S ARE FOR HATE MUNGER'S* and *KEEP YOUR HANDS OFF MY LAND MISTER GOVERNER!* Seese worried about the friendship, she told me, and sometimes laughed at the expressions Rinpoche brought home, some intact and others mangled. She'd asked him why he bothered with Les Ingler. "He likes the horses," was the explanation, and Seese let it go at that, because Rinpoche had liked horses, too, in his Tibetan-Siberian youth, and because my sister wasn't the type to, well, nag.

Still, the friendship surprised me. What could a monk have in common with a character like Les Ingler? "You watch the races on TV? At Les's house?"

"Big ones," he said. "Triple Clown."

"None bigger."

I waited for more, for some comment that might better explain the odd friendship, but, as soon as the conversation started, Rinpoche had slowed down. He was monopolizing the fifty-five-mph zone in the slow lane and seemed to have said all he was going to say on the subject of late-stage angst.

"A little ways farther up you'll see the sign on the right. Rein's. R-E-I-N-S. The Vernon exit, it's supposed to be. The directions say we turn right at the end of the exit and then left into the parking lot. It's in a kind of strip mall."

"Okay, Otto."

It wasn't until we'd escaped the highway and found the strip mall and Rinpoche had parked his new pickup way, way over at one empty end, to limit the risk of accident, I suppose, or to make the move into a parking space less complicated, that he turned to me. We sat there for a moment, looking at each other. "Otto," he said, in his teaching voice, "the horses when they turn the last one, they see the end and they run as fast as what's left for them inside. They don't leave something in the gas in the tank, see?"

"Sure, yes."

"Same for you."

"But how? First of all, there's not as much gas in the tank as there used to be. And, second, you told me many times that if I focus too much on *accomplishing* something in meditation, on getting somewhere, that would be just the ego sticking its nose in. That I should be relaxed about it, not strive for any particular goal. The last thing the horses seem to be in the stretch is relaxed."

"They forget about everything else at the end. You can see it. One-mindedness."

"So I shouldn't do anything but meditate."

"Read a little."

"What?"

"Good books. Wery wery slow, you read them. One word. Then one more word. *Lectio Divina* the Catholics call it."

The Latin had rolled off his tongue as if he were an abbot at a Trappist monastery. "It's hard to see how that connects to horses in the stretch," I said.

He pressed his lips together and for a moment I thought I'd at last managed to push him over the edge of his vast plateau of patience. Then the flash of a smile, brief and bright as sunlight knifing through an overcast sky. "Listen me."

"Listening."

"Everything now you do. Every thing. You do like you see the finish wire."

"Okay."

"You can eat. You can play the tennis. Reading the paper. You can go for the dentist to fix your teeth. And every minute, relaxed, relaxed, you see the finish line. See? You think about that this body don't belongs to you. That, one day, you leave it go. See?"

"Almost. But I don't want to think about death every minute."

He did lose patience then, slapping one hand down on the top of his leg. "Who said about the death?"

51

"Well, that was the finish line in this metaphor, it seemed to me."

A small shake of the head. "You dying every minute," he said, and while I was considering that, he added, "You living every minute, too, see?"

"No."

"You can waste time but don't waste time now, see?"

"No. I'm sorry. No. You're Zenning me again."

He crossed his arms, pursed his lips, brought his eyebrows together. Focusing, not angry. Looking for the way to reach me. Half a minute passed like that, and I was hungry and about to give up when he said, in a gentler tone, "Life has the different parts, Otto. Like a farm. You break the dirt. You plant the seed. You make sure it grows up. Then the beans or the wheat come, see. And you take them."

"The harvest."

"Yes. This is the most important part. Your part now. Harvest. See?"

"I'm ripe?" I tried.

His face bloomed. Instead of slapping himself on the leg, he slapped me on the leg. I was still taking a blood thinner after the ablation. His encouraging gesture would leave a bruise for a full week. "Ripe in the spirchal part, Otto! Good!" He put his hands up in front of his nose, palm to palm, a little space between them. "You see the horses in front of you and you have the space. Through the space you see the finish wire. Go there now, nothing else. Hard as you can, but running nice, almost relaxing. See?"

"Maybe. Yes. Thank you."

"Welcome," he said, and we stepped out of the truck and walked the length of the parking lot, physically side by side, but, in some other, invisible dimension, a thousand miles apart.

Eight

The lunch we enjoyed at Rein's New York Style Deli may say something about me I'd rather not say, but my intention in writing about these trips with Rinpoche has always been to tell the truth. Period. The truth, the actual truth, and nothing but the truth. A complicated business, however. We all look through our own dusty lenses and believe we're taking a clear snapshot of what *is*. Often, there's a major conceit involved, as though somehow we've been granted the True Vision, of ourselves and the world, and if others disagree, they must be mistaken. If I were to distill into one sentence the value of everything my brother-in-law has given me over the decades of our acquaintance, all the teachings, all of what he calls his 'wessons', all the advice and guidance, it would be that he's helped me dust off that subjective lens, at least to some degree. To see things as they are and myself as I am. Not perfectly, of course, but more clearly. I've come to believe that it's an endless process, that, as we move along the path, there are layers upon layers of grit and dust requiring a subtler and deeper cleaning of the lens.

In any case, the truth revealed by our visit to Rein's is that I've worried for years about my relationship to food. My great fear was that one day, Rinpoche—who often encouraged me to fast for a day or a few days—would tell me that the only way to take the next step on the spiritual path was to embrace a rigid regime of self-denial, something like the austere practices of the monks of most traditions. To seriously alter my great passion: eating.

I'm not obese. With the exception of a particularly difficult period of months after Jeannie passed away, I've never been more than about ten pounds overweight in my entire adult life. But most of that is due to a metabolism I inherited from three generations of hardworking North Dakota farmers, some of it to my love of tennis and walking, some of it to my vanity, and some to wanting to be attractive to Jeannie and set a good example for the kids.

I worked for almost three decades as a food editor, focusing more on everyday tasty meals than on gourmet preparations, and so it's perhaps normal that I think about food so often and enjoy my meals to a degree I'm not sure everyone shares. Still, from time to time I've worried that what I think of as 'enjoyment' should actually be called 'addiction', and I was musing along those lines as we made the walk across the parking lot and went through the front door of Rein's.

I should add here that we were traveling in the season Christians call Lent, and, while Rinpoche was not a Christian, he'd become more interested of late in some of the Catholic mystical traditions, *lectio divina* among them. On the night before we left, he and Seese and I had enjoyed dinner at one of my favorite Bronxville spots, Scalini Osteria. They'd had apple pie on the menu, and, after a large meal, I'd ordered a slice of pie with the obligatory scoop of vanilla ice cream. Seese abstained. Rinp reached across and stole a few forkfuls, but then, as we were walking home, he said, "It's went."

I hadn't heard well, and I'd drunk two glasses of wine at dinner, and so I made a weak joke. "Where did it go?"

"*Lent,* he means," Seese said. She wrapped an arm around

her husband's wide shoulders and kissed him on the cheek. "Say 'love'," she said.

"Love," Rinpoche repeated, but it sounded something like *lwuv*.

"Who loves you?" she asked.

"The beautiful woman my wife," he said. "And many many other people!"

His laugh echoed again in the street. I saw a light go on over a neighboring porch. We walked along for a bit and then he said, "We giving up dessert every other day for went, me and Otto. You never want dessert, my good wife, so doesn't matter!"

Seese kept her left arm around her husband, and Rinpoche wrapped his left arm around me and pulled me against him. "On this trip, no eating the sweet some days, okay? No dessert."

"Absolutely," I said. "A spiritual discipline."

"That's what it's for, I guess," Seese said. "We never observed Lent, though, in the family. I don't think it's a Protestant thing to give up stuff."

We walked the last hundred yards like that, three of us held close against each other in the middle of the quiet street. I remember thinking, amid the nascent terror I felt at the idea of foregoing dessert every other day, that it was one of the few times I'd actually seen my sister and Rinpoche act like lovers, like a married couple. They were never cold with each other, they never seemed to argue, but there was a certain physical reserve, at least when other people were around. I remember the warmth of that walk, the way it caused me to recall similar moments when Jeannie had been alive and the kids had been young and there had been so much physical affection among the four of us. I remember wondering if some people felt that way all the time, alone and with others, bathed in love, connected.

In any case, as you step into Rein's, there's a take-out deli to your left, with lists of tempting sandwiches on overhead boards, and, to your right, after you move past displays of sweets and pickles, the host stand. This arrangement is both unfair and, probably, from a business standpoint, wise, because those opening moments place certain images in your mind. Before you get too full to think about dessert, you've seen the sweets. Cheesecake, chocolates, baklava, pies, those devilishly delicious little concoctions called ruggalach, all of them arrayed on shelves behind glass. For me, there was something almost erotic about it; the attraction was that strong. Remembering our Lenten pledge, I actually tried to turn my eyes away, but as the hostess led us past a woman-sized model of the Statue of Liberty and into a bar area called the "Off-off Broadway," I couldn't keep from sneaking one quick glance to my left at the German Chocolate Cake, the beautiful round bulk of it, one slice missing.

The menu at Rein's is extravagant: chopped liver sandwiches, knishes, borscht, latkes, soups, salads, appetizers, and a line of drinks and desserts running in smaller print across the top. Rinpoche glanced at it for five seconds and set it aside, while I tormented myself over whether to order the brisket plate or the chopped liver sandwich, how to maximize my pleasure, knowing, as I did, that we wouldn't be back at Rein's for weeks or months, perhaps years, possibly ever, and that the likelihood of finding a real Jewish deli on the outskirts of say, Richmond or Raleigh, was slim at best. In my mid-twenties, I'd moved from North Dakota to New York, which was not that different than moving from Earth to Saturn. One of the many dimensions of that intraplanetary transmigration had to do with the presence of Jewish people. In North Dakota farm country there were none, or next to none. In New York there were many. In time, Jeannie and I came to have a number of close Jewish friends, some of them non-practicing and others devout. Both of us developed an affection for what I suppose might be called their 'culture', not the religious beliefs, per se, but the love of books and learning, the unique and sometimes sardonic humor, the emphasis on time with friends and family . . . and the food.

So it was important to maximize the opportunity Rein's offered.

Our waitress returned. Melanie was her name, a young woman just about the age of my daughter, with delicate tattoos on each forearm, an array of small rings in her left ear, and a lovely warm manner. "All set?" she asked.

Rinpoche asked for a tuna sandwich on wheat bread and a glass of lemonade, and, after one last perusal, one final moment of indecision, I went with the lox and bagel special. And then, as an afterthought, "And a chocolate egg cream, please."

Rinpoche was watching me, smiling, understanding all of it. I offered an apologetic shrug for breaking my every-other-day Lenten fast. "It's a drink, not dessert, exactly."

He laughed. "What I like is the pickles," he said, pulling one from a plastic dish and taking a bite, and in the process, absolving me. "At home, when I was the boy, my mother used to make them."

"Jeannie loved pickles. Both times when she was pregnant she had a craving for pickles. We had a whole shelf of the fridge devoted to various kinds."

Rinpoche said, for the thousandth time, how much he missed her, then he stood up and headed off toward the bathroom and I looked around. Decorating the walls were framed tributes to New York City—old magazine covers showing the skyline, scorecards from famous sporting events at the famous stadiums, caricatures of Derek Jeter and Ed Koch. My eyes shifted. Two tables away sat one of those poor souls who weighed twice what a healthy man his size would weigh, who had three plates in front of him, and who was shoveling food into his mouth with a kind of absent-minded urgency I'd seen in other obese diners. I turned my gaze rightward, out the front windows. *Hungry ghost* was the Buddhist expression, and it referred, not only to food, but to attention, sex, distraction, any substance or activity that was pursued with an insatiable frenzy. There was no bottom to that well. No amount of food would satisfy whatever it was that haunted the poor guy, and yet he'd keep trying and trying, day after day, meal after snack after meal, no matter what it did to him, physically and otherwise. Drugs, alcohol, cigarettes, pornography, talk, work, attention, shopping, power, money, cars, designer purses, expensive watches, clothes, jewelry, sex—there were so many false roads along which you could try to pursue the ultimate satisfaction.

"Nothing good comes out of guilt," Tom had said, and I believed that. Still, I felt a twinge of guilt about the degree to which I thought about food. My eyes returned briefly to the obese man, as if he were some kind of message from the gods, a flawed mirror. I made myself look away again.

Rinpoche sat opposite me, the food arrived. We made a little small talk with Melanie, who told us what the tattoos meant—names of her four children—and that, if she and her husband could afford it, she'd have eight kids, or twelve. "The gift of gifts," she called them, and smiled and went off to her duties.

"Nice person," Rinpoche said when she left. "High soul."

"Good mother, I bet."

He nodded. "Means more than anything, having the good

mother, Otto. Means you don't go all the time in your life looking for knowing you are the person you supposed to be."

I thought about my own mother: pleasant, dutiful, kind
enough, but never warm. The heavy man to my right ordered
two desserts.

"Hindu people say if you live the good life, you find, next
time, the good wound. Good mother."

"*Womb,*" I said. "Womb, not wound. And then?"

Rinpoche laughed, chewed, sipped his lemonade. "Then
someday you rest."

"That's it, then? Rest? That's the goal?"

"Rest in peace," he said, and laughed in a way no one else I
knew would have laughed at those words. "What means in
America, Otto?"

"It's what you ask for people who have died."

"*Quies,*" he said.

"That's the second time you've said something in Latin today."

"Reading the Catholic stuff, man."

"Really?"

"Sure. They know some things, some of them. Merton.
Keating. Big souls!"

"It's hard for me to match the idea of rest with the idea of
racing toward the finish line."

Rinpoche ate for a bit, savoring the food as he always did,
but somehow not in the way I savored it, as if he appreciated
but did not need it. I found myself wondering what his mother
must have been like. He'd never told me much about her—a
few comments wrapped in nostalgic smiles—and I promised
myself I'd ask about her as we drove south. "If you watch the
horses in the slow motion, you see how much they relaxing."

"Really?"

"Sure, yes. Watch next time. The way the muscles move. The wegs and feet. You have to watch with the camera on swow."

The obese man finished his meal, quickly, urgently, paid in cash, struggled to his feet and made his way, with a great deal of difficulty, between two tables and out the door. I watched him move across the parking lot, every step an exertion, the act of climbing into his white SUV looking like some kind of stress test in a cardiac lab. I tried to imagine the self-consciousness he must live with, the looks and stares and comments he had to endure, the embarrassment of his children, if he had children. The price he paid for his devotion to food. I'd seen enough addicts in my life to have long ago stopped judging them. It wasn't a moral issue for me—not unless you lied, stole, or mugged to support your habit—it was just sad. A desperate chase for satisfaction that ended, almost always, in misery.

Still, maybe to spite the cautionary voice, I broke my Lenten promise again and ordered dessert. I told myself I'd go two straight days without any sweets, to compensate. The sight of the German Chocolate Cake had been etched into my brain in a certain way, and had remained there like a promise while I ate the fresh lox and fresh bagel and onion and tomato and cream cheese and drank the egg cream in a few big gulps. When Melanie brought over a healthy slice of cake with her big smile, Rinpoche reached across and took a forkful from my plate and moved it around in his mouth and made humming noises.

That, really, was all that happened at Rein's—the sight of the obese man, the talk of pickles and mothers and slow-motion videos of thoroughbreds in the homestretch, the German Chocolate Cake. Not much, really. And yet there was a way in which those moments and that conversation would stay with me all the way down the eastern seaboard and for months afterward. I suppose you could say that I *chewed* on them, worried them, probed them. *Quies,* the Hungry Ghost, love of children, a warm mother, my own urges—there was so much there, and it would keep coming back to me as we traveled, as though I were learning a new language and needed to hear it spoken again and again.

I finished every crumb of the dessert, scraped the sweet frosting from my plate, left four one-hundred-dollar bills folded in half beneath my water glass, and, on the way out, paid the cashier with a credit card. On impulse, I grabbed a bar of halvah, too, and the cashier—Sammie was her name—told me she'd tried it for the first time recently, and loved it. "It's like a Reese's," she said. I nodded, smiled, tipped her, too, lavishly, and we stepped out into the cool October air.

"You drive now, Otto," Rinpoche said. "The big trucks in New York, they scare me."

Nine

Remembering my dad going back and forth all day on his Massey Ferguson 150—tilling, planting, harvesting, 'throwing down', as he put it, a cover crop for winter—I used to believe that country people like us were the kings and queens of patience. The slow-growing crops, the endless Dakota winters, the long drives for school, errands, sporting events, or doctors' visits—fast as we might go on the empty highways, it was ultimately pointless to rush through our days, and that bred in us a tendency toward the methodical and deliberate. The blessed ability, as Hesse's Siddhartha put it, to wait.

But, after moving to New York, the capital of hurry and frenzy, and after commuting to Manhattan and working there for thirty years, I came to realize that, in order to survive in the City, you had to have a deep well of patience, too. Not three-foot snows and durum wheat and straight-highways patience, but the patience of subway and train delays, long lines for concerts, crowded sidewalks, world-class traffic.

I was reminded of the urban version of patience when, after leaving Rein's and cruising along nicely for two hours down I-84, I-91, and I-95, we reached the Bronx. An overhead electronic sign informed us that there was construction on the George Washington Bridge (when is there *not* construction on the GW bridge?), and a traffic jam for the ten miles approaching it from the north. We weren't actually going over the bridge on this leg of the trip, but that didn't matter: in order to reach the Henry Hudson Parkway and West Side Highway, my preferred route into Manhattan, we had to get excruciatingly close to the GW, and were required to take the very last exit in New York to avoid being funneled across the Hudson and into New Jersey. Approaching that exit, we sat in traffic for one hour and fifty-six minutes.

During that time, with the big trucks squeezing close against us, and gaunt men begging between lanes, with the brake lights, exhaust fumes, and views of stone and brick apartment buildings broken eventually by a glimpse of the magnificent skyline to our left, Rinpoche sat calmly in the passenger seat, hands folded in his lap, eyes forward. I didn't sense from him so much as a ripple of impatience, and I have to say that, while I didn't exactly enjoy creeping along for two hours like that, I handled it better than I would have in my premeditation days. Sitting still for an hour every morning is the mental equivalent of lifting weights or running for an hour every day. Do that for years and you can't help but build muscle, interior or exterior. Plus, it wasn't like we had a schedule to keep. I figured I had forty-some hours to show Rinpoche the city—that was our rough plan—and then we were headed south, with not much on the calendar and, so far, no fixed route.

Eventually, we reached the exit for West 4th Street and zigged and zagged through Lower Manhattan until we found the parking garage that had accepted my online payment. From there—Mott Street—it was a short walk to the lodging Seese had booked for us, a modern six-story establishment called the NobleDEN Hotel (correct spelling!) on Grand Street, squeezed between Chinatown and Little Italy. That area might be my fa-

vorite part of the city, a festival of life, with the hydrants painted green, white, and red, the old tenements and fire escapes
balanced above cafes and restaurants, the fruit and vegetable
and seafood sellers, the acupuncture shops, the T-shirt shops,
women hawking knock-off purses on the corners, the industri-
ousness of the residents and the curiosity of the tourists. A lot
of good food, too. No skyscrapers there, it's all Old World, the
side streets narrow, crooked, and choked with parked cars, the
storefronts changing every few years to reflect the latest trends
in food, clothing, or body care. There's the fragrance of hard
history in spots, too, because, a hundred years earlier, those
apartments had been filled with people who'd fled the poverty
of southern Italy and the starvation and political turmoil in
China, just as, at the northern end of the island, the apartments
had been filled by people fleeing slavery. North and South,
Manhattan has *want* at its foundation: wanting freedom, wanting to eat, wanting work, wanting simply to be left alone. Like
the rest of the country, New York City doesn't always fulfill the
promise it offers, but the promise remains, and to this day the
five boroughs draw people to New York's gritty bosom from
every part of the earth.

After we'd checked into our tidy room with a view down
onto the lively chaos of Grand Street, Rinpoche and I decided
we needed a walk. The big meal at Rein's and all that sitting in
the truck were calling us back out to the street. In a breezy
March chill we headed north up Broadway, leaving Little Italy
behind and entering SoHo. We made a right turn on East 9th
and walked all the way over to Avenue D, then made another
right, with the Jacob Riis House and the other huge brick pro-
jects to our left. Another right on Delancey, just where the Wil-
liamsburg Bridge makes landfall on the island, and back to the
Bowery and Mott and the fruit sellers we went.

Six miles in all, that hour and a half walk took us across Bleecker Street where Robert DeNiro had grown up and Herman Melville had lived, past SoHo cafes and boutiques where you could pay twelve dollars for a coffee and pastry and a hundred dollars for a blouse, through Tomkins Park, where dogs large and small frolicked in fenced areas and kids dribbled basketballs on the cold courts, then down through the Alphabet Avenues—the sense of *want* still there, after all these years; not just a foundation, not just history, but a living reality on those tar lanes. We went from apparently well educated, well dressed, confident young couples, to heroin addicts stumbling out of alleys and drunks lying on cardboard on the frigid sidewalk in soiled pants and windburned faces, suffering mightily. Grandmothers pushing strollers. Old men with walkers. Couples holding hands, men playing dominoes in the wintry air. Rich, poor, and everything in-between. In Little Italy you can get a slice of pizza for four dollars. On Avenue D, a slice goes for 99 cents, because the system charges what the market will bear, giving and taking according to an invisible algorithm we've lived with so long we don't even think about it, the world markets lifting some of us up to great heights and pressing others down hard against the grimy sidewalks of poverty. I thought of Shelsa again, and wondered if we Americans had made a kind of religion of our economic system. To speak out against it, to question it even mildly, tentatively, to suggest a few adjustments as Shelsa was apparently doing—all that had become, in many circles, nothing less than blasphemy. Political suicide in all but a couple of congressional districts. A person like me, one of its greatest beneficiaries, felt a wash of guilt even thinking about capitalism's imperfections. But I felt a wash of guilt, too, walking through the poorer sections of the city I loved. I could *feel* the want there, the systemic injustice; anyone with half a

65

heart could feel it. As if it were a great weight balanced on top of my head, I could feel my own wealth, too, and part of me wanted to walk along handing out hundred-dollar bills. But that would have been like tossing coins from a royal limousine.

So, I found myself wondering again what, exactly, was one supposed to do? Ignore the suffering? Send a check and head off to the tennis club for lunch? Starve oneself to keep a few others from starving? Justify it all by blaming the victims? Indulge, protest, a little of both? At one point, after we'd made the corner onto Delancey and were heading west again in the last of the afternoon light, I said to my brother-in-law: "We're probably going to spend on dinner tonight what some people we just walked past spend on food in a week."

He pursed his lips. A kid walking the other way with his father said, "Dad, that guy has a dress on!"

I waited, musing, stewing.

After half a block Rinpoche said, "Now you starting, maybe Otto, to see."

That was all I got. I wanted to tell him that I had seen, had been seeing, for decades. But perhaps that wasn't quite true.

The other thing I got was a twinge in my right lower back and right hip, consequence of all those post-ablation weeks on the couch. I mentioned it to Rinpoche, thought of trying to get a massage, decided against it. But I remembered that once, years before, when we'd all come to town as a family to celebrate Natasha's birthday, my son Anthony, the football player, had suffered a bad back spasm and, out of desperation really, I'd taken him to a massage place in a basement level on Grand Street. Jeannie thought I was crazy—we didn't know the place, there weren't any reviews—but, after being worked on for thirty minutes by a middle-aged Chinese man half his size, Anthony came bounding up the stairs claiming a miracle cure. Near the end of our long walk now, Rinpoche and I were approaching that exact place—from all appearances unchanged.

As I walked past the top of the white metal stairs, a rat came scurrying along, saw or sensed me, made a quick U-turn and scurried back out into the gutter. I laughed.

Later that evening, when Rinpoche and I were sitting at a table in Il Cortile on Mulberry Street, having been served a free dish of pasta carbonara by a host named Vincenzo because "we keeping you waiting too long," I asked my traveling companion if he had any urge to return to Italy. He'd greeted Vincenzo in perfect Italian and, in stunned disbelief, Vincenzo had replied with four or five sentences I did not understand.

"I was happy there, Otto," Rinpoche said.

"You're happy everywhere."

"It made me happy to see the Dalai Lama and to talk with him little bit."

"And the Pope."

He nodded, savored a bite of pasta, looked around him at the other diners. "Shelsa and the little boy there—"

"Tomasso."

"They going to make the whirl a little better maybe. Soon."

"The world could use some improvement."

More nodding, another bite, a sip of wine. "This gonna be your work now, to be helping them."

Vincenzo came and took away our mostly empty plates, and a few seconds later, a waiter brought the main course. I was already full.

Rinpoche grinned across the table at me.

"I'll help in any way I can."

"Big way."

"If you say so, sure. I love Shelsa, you know that. I love being an uncle. I've loved watching her grow up."

Rinpoche seemed then as if he were about to say something more on the subject—my future work, a return to Italy, Shelsa's karma. He hesitated, looked down at his eggplant parmigiana so long that the waiter came back and asked if it everything was okay. "Good, good, yes," Rinpoche said, and when the waiter left us, Rinpoche began to eat, and whatever he was thinking of saying remained unsaid.

I would, however, have reason to remember that moment.

I managed to eat half my dinner—a succulent *Puttanesca*—and then, enjoying the next-to-the-last sip of wine, asked my good brother-in-law if there was anything special he wanted to do the next day. The point of the visit, after all, was to show him a city I knew intimately and one he barely knew at all. "Except for when you ran the weight-loss clinic for a couple months, you've never spent much time in Manhattan, and I've worked here all my adult life. Whatever you want, we'll do. Museums, the Park, more walking. Tomorrow, late afternoon, we should head out."

"I saw the bus," he said, suddenly excited, turning his head side to side as if mimicking a tourist checking out the sights. "You sit up on the roof and they take you for a ride and tell you what you seeing!"

I swallowed, sought refuge in the wine. Of all the possible entertainments offered in the City, spending hours on a tour bus, with some guide making inane jokes and pointing out the number of floors in the Empire State Building, sat at the very bottom of the list. Above only the thought of sitting on the upper level in the cold.

"You sure?" I asked Rinpoche, hoping he wasn't.

"Sure, sure, Otto. No more walking for your back, and I can know New York pretty good if we taking the bus!"

68

Ten

Before Rinpoche and I sat for our morning meditation, before I left a tip of several hundred dollars for the person who would clean our room, before we walked a few blocks southwest to a sparkling new coffeeshop on Canal Street called Coffee on Cannal (two n's), where, if you wished (we did not), they could infuse your cup of Joe with all manner of cannabis-related tinctures, and where they made the most delicious cinnamon bun I have ever eaten, before we took the subway to Times Square (Rinpoche on the Uptown Express asking the dreadlocked man sitting beside him what he was eating from his Styrofoam cup, "Black beans and cabbage," the man replied, smiling, and Rinpoche patted him on the knee and said, "Good, good, delicious. I like it wery much!"), and before we stood for a full cold hour waiting for the tour bus to pull to the curb on 42nd Street, I sat at the desk in room 203 and wrote a check to the organization I'd volunteered with for twenty years, slipped the check into an envelope, folded the envelope, and put it into the zippered inside pocket of my leather jacket.

En route from the subway station to the tour bus stop, we'd passed a man handing out advertisements for a 'gentlemen's club'—one of the world's great euphemisms. Without realizing what it advertised, or even glancing at the card, Rinpoche had taken one—out of kindness, I suppose—and for some reason he held on to it, letting it flap back and forth in the air as he moved his arms. I waited for him to examine it, to ask me questions, maybe to suggest a visit ("What is, Otto? Can we see?") but he only swung it back and forth through the air as if cleaning off the dust. So I said nothing.

It was chilly and uncrowded up there on what Rinpoche called the bus's 'roof', most patrons preferring the warmer, enclosed level below. As he always did, hot weather and cold, the good monk wore only one of his two gold-trimmed maroon robes, but he did put something on his shaved head: a round, rimless hat Seese had knitted him from forest green wool. It was too small, however, and perched there like a yarmulke. I was hatless, wearing a sweater and a leather jacket, sunglasses for light-sensitive eyes. It turned out that I was behind the times again: the human tour guide had been replaced by a recorded narration delivered through red plastic earphones. A big improvement, as far as I was concerned, though I'm sure the tour guides who'd lost their jobs would disagree. We chose seats near the back, wrapped ourselves in the blankets the bus company offered, put in the earphones, and the big red vehicle trundled off in a belch of black smoke.

North we went, north along Broadway at first, and then onto Central Park West, passing the Hearst Building, the red brick former cancer hospital (now luxury condominiums) where Ulysses S. Grant had died (the turrets at the corners rounded, the recorded narration informed us, because, in those years, people believed germs lingered in the corners of the room), passing the places where Lucky Luciano and John Lennon had been shot to death, rolling past Trump Tower and the statue to Christopher Columbus, past a long-gone African American settlement on Central Park called Seneca Village. Across the street from it stood luxury apartments rented by the likes of Steven Spielberg, Steve Jobs, and Yoko Ono (the narrator mentioned that Madonna's application had been denied), then, farther up on the right, St. John the Divine Cathedral ('St. John the Unfinished', it was sometimes called), and the buildings of Columbia University.

We then turned east on 125th, a wide, thriving commercial street I'd walked along countless times in all kinds of weather, and an area that had once been at the heart of the Harlem Renaissance. The bus company had advertised its tour as 'hop-on, hop-off', so, near a statue of Adam Clayton Powell, we exercised our right, stepping down onto the sidewalk just as two fifty-something women, walking arm-in-arm and carrying large bright purses, were dissolving into laughter. They weren't laughing at the man in the maroon robe and green yarmulke, or at his cold-looking, sunglasses-wearing companion; they were just laughing, uproariously, at something one of them had said, it seemed. Surrounding themselves with a cloud of mirth amid the business of the day and the complexities of human life. I half-expected my brother-in-law to go up to them and ask if he could share the joke. I'd half-expected him to ask the fellow on the subway if he might have a taste of his cabbage-and-bean lunch. Rinpoche was like that. He seemed long ago to have torn down the ordinary walls we erect between each other out of fear or decorum or shyness or habit. If *I'd* asked someone on the subway what he was eating, then touched him on the knee, it would have seemed vaguely criminal, but with Rinp, somehow, it came off as perfectly natural. Years ago I'd thought he was just new to American life and missing the leave-me-alone clues, but that wasn't it. He had the great gift of being able to connect at a deeper level, human to human, asking nothing, unafraid, unselfconscious, looking beyond the surfaces, expecting the best from people. And strangers, most of them, responded accordingly.

I mention this because, as we walked north toward the offices of Gotham Reads, I was thinking about a college friend Natasha had brought home for a weekend years earlier, a young man who lacked Rinpoche's gift for simple, straightforward human connection. A lover perhaps, we'd never asked, though Natasha's friendship with him lasted only a month or two. Laurence was his name. Parisian dad, American mom. On the one evening Laurence visited us in Bronxville, it so happened that I'd gotten home late for dinner because the tutoring had gone longer than usual and there had been a delay in the Harlem line. Laurence made a comment that had stuck with me, and not in a good way. "A little bit of *noblesse oblige,* ey, Mr. R?" was what he said, speaking of my volunteer work. The tone was sardonic, college-age-wise, as if the act of helping young people learn to read and write well was actually nothing more than a fake gift, given from on high, an elaborately disguised condescension, a gesture of conceit. "A bit of the white-savior thing, ey?"

Taken aback, but not wanting to cause discomfort to my daughter, I responded in a neutral way, "Reading was so helpful to our kids," or something like that, and Natasha quickly steered the conversation elsewhere.

But I remembered that remark. I had volunteered because I did, in fact, know how important reading was; because it had, in fact, helped my own children have good experiences in school; and because I was trying to find a way to 'give back', as the saying has it, to kids who needed help with the subjects. Human to human. Rinpoche-style. But because the kids I tutored in Harlem were mostly black and mostly poor, Laurence had somehow twisted my work there into a bad thing, and that kind of twisting, it seemed to me, had become commonplace now, ordinary human decency stained with every manner of overanalysis. Guilt applied with a broad brush. I was pondering that societal twist as Rinpoche and I walked up to the Gotham Reads offices—which I was surprised to find closed on that morning—pondering what someone like Laurence would say about the Giving Project. I was sure he'd find a way to make it into a negative thing, an insult, an ego indulgence, *noblesse oblige*.

I knocked, rang the bell, waited, and at last slipped the envelope through the mail slot. I knew the check would reach the people I wanted to have it, and I suspected that, though I hadn't tutored there in several years, someone might recognize my unusual last name. I was confident in the worthiness of the organization, had even corresponded for a while with some of the kids after they left high school and went on to college, jobs, and adult life. It was a large amount—I won't say how much—and so I wasn't at all unhappy about the relative anonymity. No fuss. No awkwardness. No twisting of my motivations. No mocking voice of Laurence in my inner ear. Money to help good people who'd been doing a good thing for decades in all the City's five boroughs. Period.

We caught the next tour bus that came along, and rode south out of Spanish Harlem, past the mansions of the Upper East Side, the elegant stone palaces where Frick and Mellon and Carnegie had once lived, museums now, all of them. The park with its bare trees and silenced fountains, the beautiful white bulk of the Metropolitan Museum, then the Plaza Hotel and the neighboring shops facing the southern end of the park, boutiques where you could pay, for a small antique vase or a few suits of clothes, a sum close to what the Gotham Reads people had just received.

Who wouldn't think about money on a trip like that? How could you fail to muse about wealth and how it was made and what was done with it? Andrew Carnegie considered his ordinary laborers to be a lower class of human being, forced them to work twelve-hour days, and then donated ninety per cent of his massive fortune to fund libraries and colleges. The Rockefellers and Sloans and Mellons blended business acumen and the sweat and suffering of millions of workers into a delicious cake, pieces of which would be enjoyed for generations.

Noblesse oblige, all of it, I was thinking. Human imperfection. Greed and generosity co-existing in one mind.

The bus finished its big loop behind Times Square, and Rinpoche and I disembarked and walked around for a while, past neon billboards that cost millions to rent, and that sold overpriced underwear and nail polish, past the beggars and business people, the limos and cabs, the retired couples in for a week from Wyoming or Arkansas, staring at the top floors of buildings. After a puzzled perusal, Rinpoche had finally dropped the gentlemen's club card into a trash bin, but I was afraid that, in his innocence, my companion was going to ask to see the inside of one of the clubs, so I decided to pre-empt him. "Rinp. A question."

"Shoot me," he answered, one of his many small misinterpretations of American idiom.

I had six thousand dollars in cash in the left inside pocket of my leather jacket, a checkbook in the right inside pocket. "What is money?"

He laughed, as I somehow knew he would. "The thing you get for workin'," he said.

"Right. I mean, in the bigger picture. Karma-wise, or whatever. What is it?"

A pause, a small lift at the corners of his mouth, "Lets you live," he said.

"Okay. But even bigger. How does it bear on the spiritual life?"

He stopped and faced me for a second or two, looking into my eyes as if searching for the root of the question, then he took my arm and led me into a Five Guys burger place a few steps away. Confused, I watched him go up to the cashier and ask for a drink, saw him give her roughly twice what the drink cost, then take the cup she handed him and walk back to the machine that dispensed a variety of sugary liquids. He pressed the cup against the metal piece and half-filled it with ice, then turned and met my eyes. "Listen me, Otto." He moved the cup sideways, pressed a button, and poured an inch of root beer into the cup, turned and showed it to me. "Not enough money, you have to always think about, worry about, try to get more so you can eat, so your family had a place to sleep. Hard to have energy for the spirchal life."

"Okay."

He then pressed the cup against the metal piece and filled it to the brim, but kept pressing, root beer pouring over the sides and over his fingers. He stopped finally, and looked at me again. "Too much money, also make the spirchal life hard. You always think about how to keep it, make it bigger, see? You worry when it goes a little small."

"Okay."

He tilted the cup sideways, poured out some of the contents, and brought the root beer level down to an inch from the lip. "Enough money but not too much, good place to get on the bus for the spirchal tour, see? Not the only place, but maybe the good one."

"Sure," I said, "Okay. Fine. A little too general for me, and plenty of exceptions, but okay. I get the basic idea: best not to think about it all the time."

"Mommy, the funny man in the bathrobe is wasting soda!" a smart little guy behind us yelled. A future Laurence.

75

Eleven

When we awakened the next morning, it was snowing. Medium-sized flakes angled down over Grand Street like a shifting lace curtain between the hotel and the six-story brick buildings across the way. Pedestrians wearing raincoats and down jackets leaned into the weather as they walked, some holding umbrellas, some hustling from cab to doorway in suit and tie or good dresses, all of them, I imagined, life-toughened New Yorkers accustomed to the slushy winters and humid summers, the traffic noise and subway grime, the brusque manners of the street that could sometimes suddenly mutate into violence, or soften to wry humor. "You'll be living with us on the farm," Seese had said during our lunch at Kabul, and I wondered how I'd deal with that after those many years of city life, what I'd do all day, where I'd go to escape the brutal north-plains cold.

And how, from there, was I supposed to help Shelsa and Tomasso in their life's work?

Staring out the hotel window while Rinpoche showered and shaved, I was thinking that so much of our energies in the modern world went toward making life easier and more comfortable, inventing dishwashers and microwaves, recliners, raised-bed gardens, mattresses that adjusted to our weight, shape, and sleeping habits. But even with all that, whether we farmed in North Dakota or commuted to a cubicle in Manhattan, life always seemed to find new ways to require of us a degree of toughness. "Just one thing after another," my father was fond of saying when his fields were parched by drought or flooded by rain, or when his tractor popped a gasket or his tiller snapped a tine. Just one thing after another. Wet snow, when you were expecting a pleasant morning stroll to a nice breakfast place. Cancer, when you were imagining a comfortable retirement with your spouse. War, when you thought the world, Europe at least, had seen enough of that.

When Rinpoche was finished, I took my turn in the bathroom and then we sat for an hour in the room's two hard chairs. As he'd counseled me over the years, I simply tried to let my thoughts settle, not to chase after them, whether pleasant or disturbing, not to force them in any particular direction, not to lose patience with the wanderings of my own mind. "Just be calm," he said, "watch, don't push." It worked. Again. By the time the alarm on my cell phone sounded, signaling the end of the session, I was able to zip up my suitcase and roll it into the hallway, refreshed, aware, not carrying the world upon my shoulders.

We left my suitcase and Rinpoche's leather satchel near the front desk and asked the young tattooed man there if he'd be kind enough to watch them. By then the snow had turned to rain. "Want we bring you back the breakfast?" Rinp asked. The young man shook his head, smiled, pointed to a coffee cup and a half-eaten egg McMuffin on the counter in front of him.

On the street, after walking in a big square looking for something that seemed right and different and getting nothing but wet, we found a place called Baz Bagel, and I had yet another good serving of lox and bagels for something close to $40 for two. On the way back to the hotel, I asked Rinpoche if the reason I liked Jewish food so much might have to do with a past lifetime. The idea, I have to admit, had been put into my head by a psychic in Leadville, Colorado, on another of our roadtrips.

"Sure, Otto," Rinp said.

"I feel a strong connection with certain things, certain people. Jeannie, of course. I often wondered: were we friends in another life? Siblings, neighbors?"

"Yes," he said.

"Do you feel that with Seese?"

He turned his head to look at me for a moment. The rain had eased by then, but the air was raw, and we'd ended up in a small knot of people waiting for the light to change so we could cross Mulberry Street. "Ed told me focus on the road," Rinpoche said.

"Ed? Who's Ed?"

"The man who teach me to drive few years ago. 'Focus on the road,' he was saying, many times. 'Maybe look back in the mirror a little sometime, but focus on the road, Mister Volya'."

"*Driver's Ed*, you mean?"

"Yes," Rinpoche said, "Ed."

By then the light had changed and we were crossing.

"Can you remember your past lives?"

At that, a woman walking close ahead—she was holding a tiny, wet, white-haired dog against her chest and wearing a transparent plastic poncho—actually turned all the way around and looked at us. She smiled. I nodded. Rinpoche didn't seem to notice.

As we moved forward in the loosening crowd, I turned my face toward him, waiting for an answer, and felt my foot slide an inch or two along the sidewalk. I looked down to see the wet brown smear, and then I spent several minutes at the curb, scraping the sole of my running shoe on the sharp edge, rubbing the shoe on a patch of grass beside a small tree, even splashing it in a puddle and wiping it some more to make certain I wouldn't bring the smelly substance into the hotel or onto the floor of the new truck. Rinpoche watched, smiling, nodding encouragement, but didn't answer the question. Eyes on the road, I guess; that was the answer.

A few more steps and we were at the door of the Noble-Den. "How was breakfast?" the man behind the desk asked cheerfully.

"Expensive but good," I told him. "And I stepped in something a dog left. Wiped it off, though, no worries."

He laughed and said, "Man, in this town, you really gotta watch where you're going."

Twelve

We required the better part of fifteen minutes to retrieve our vehicle from the garage and get on the road. The parking operation was housed in a very tight space—at least judging from the ground floor—with an entrance and exit opening onto Mott Street and a string of cars waiting to be checked in and shuttled down into what must have been a much larger space below. Thanks to all the time we'd spent in each other's company, and the trips we'd been on together, I was by then more or less accustomed to Rinpoche's sudden changes of heart. It had taken me a while, but I'd come to understand that the sudden course-changes, some large, some small, were part of a larger teaching. "Wessons" he would have called them. He was trying to train me to live in the present, which, it seemed, was next to impossible for an inhabitant of the modern world. I told myself—and often tried to tell him—that, in order to survive, we had to depend on plans. If you wanted to have your teeth cleaned, you had to make an appointment with the dentist months in advance. If you wished to take a vacation, you had to tell your boss ahead of time, make reservations at a hotel, choose a route, pay for a flight, and such things couldn't be done at the last minute . . . not if you wanted to secure the flight, route, or hotel at the top of your list. To a limited extent, he agreed; certainly his speaking appearances were scheduled ahead of time (though—one of my sister's quirks—I often wasn't privy to that information). When we traveled, Seese usually made our hotel reservations, and those reservations determined our route, but much of the time I wasn't told more than a day in advance where we'd be spending the night, and sometimes the route was changed without more than a few hours' notice. Almost daily, Rinpoche—and/or my sister—would surprise me in one way or another, as if to underline the fact that, while we could make all the plans we wanted, we could never really know what would happen a month, a week, or even a few seconds in the future.

I accepted this, in theory. In practice, it often immersed me in a hot, bubbling pool of irritation. Still, over time, I'd come to admit that I was continually living in the future, mentally planning out my hours, days, and weeks as a kind of hedge against life's unpredictabilities. Deep down, I seemed to believe that if I thought carefully enough about the day ahead—we'd drive here, eat a certain kind of food, stay at a certain hotel—those thoughts would serve as a guarantee. If something upset the plan, I'd feel, at that same depth, unfairly treated. Why was the Asian restaurant closed, when I'd looked it up online and its website promised it would be open? Why did an enormous traffic delay on I-91 make me miss the first half of one of Anthony's football games when he'd been playing against Dartmouth? Why was the restaurant out of rhubarb pie, when I'd had my mind set on it?

Why did my wife die at age 51, when we'd planned a long and happy retirement together?

These 'wessons' were sometimes given by the Universe, and sometimes by my be-robed brother-in-law and eccentric sister, but I confess that, even after the loss of my wife, I never seemed to master the idea that served as the title of Ram Dass's famous book: *Be Here Now*. I kept imagining my way down the road, kept making plans, both essential and needless. And real life, the real world, kept shifting this way and that beneath me, as if I were a very small boat in very rough seas.

In Manhattan, the surprise was that, overnight, Rinpoche appeared to have lost his interest in driving. "No, no, you, Otto," he said forcefully, when I'd tipped the fellow who'd brought the silver pickup into view. "You drive now!"

Out through the Holland Tunnel we went, and then south on that gloriously traffic-choked highway called The New Jersey Turnpike. The rain faucet had been turned on again, a steady drizzle that occluded the roadside scenery, such as it was, and made me glad we hadn't taken the separate lanes where big trucks were allowed. With Rinpoche, it was always hard to tell when he was sleeping and when he was meditating, but one of those was going on in the passenger seat and, though curious about the war news, I left the radio off so as not to disturb him.

We went along, headed—unless things changed—toward the Delaware Bridge, the nation's capital, and points south.

Traveling behind a bright yellow station wagon, 1980s vintage, with a "GOD BLESS EVERYONE, NO EXCEPTIONS!" bumper sticker, I found myself thinking of Shelsa, and what Rinpoche had called her 'trouble', and here is a part of the story where I'll venture into territory some will find difficult to embrace. Let me say in advance that I understand your skepticism. For many years I also held to the more traditional view of life, to the belief that certain things were possible and other things were not; that, while there were good and evil people, the good end of the scale had a kind of limit to it. You could be generous, centered, and loving; you could do good deeds; you could nurture your marriage with love and raise your kids to be thoughtful citizens. You could perhaps invent a medicine that rescued millions of people from great suffering. Anything more that—so-called 'sainthood,' 'enlightenment,' or 'self-realization'—belonged to the imaginary fields my sister plowed from her sagging little house in Paterson. It belonged to the daily Horoscope column, to the 'seers' and 'psychics' and 'mediums' who took your ten, twenty, or fifty dollars and told you that a great fortune awaited you, very soon; that you'd been Cleopatra or Socrates in a past incarnation and were destined for some great fame or hardship in this one; that the love of your life would be found in a restaurant, perhaps a Chinese buffet, sometime in this calendar year; or that you'd soon be called upon to help bring justice and peace to the world . . . and you could hear more details for another twenty dollars. "Wait, someone is speaking from the other dimension. I see an "R". Do you know anyone who's crossed over and who'd had a name with an "R" in it during this incarnation?"

To my mind, all that stuff belonged to the fake spiritual masters who forced themselves on their adoring acolytes or made claims about their own enlightenment that proved, over time, to be wishful thinking, sly advertising, or both.

This part of the story will seem, for some readers, to fit into that squeaky drawer, but I shall not be deterred from telling it.

Even before she gave birth to Shelsa, my sister had told me more than once that she felt she was pregnant with 'a special being.' I humored her. Parents always believe their kids are special, that they're going to do great things in the world, live a life superior to that of the people who raised them. And Seese had been saying strange things for so long that I wouldn't have been terribly surprised if she claimed her child was destined to be the next Queen of Iceland.

After Shelsa's birth, Jeannie and I went to North Dakota for ten days to see the baby. We took Anthony and Natasha along to meet their only cousin. Naturally, we all made a fuss over the child, taking turns holding her, saying how beautiful she was, how alert, commenting on her dark, almost violet, eyes, plump cheeks, and the shock of black hair that stood up from the middle of her scalp. We helped out the new parents where we could—making meals, running errands, holding our niece while Seese and Rinpoche bathed, meditated, or took a walk together in the fields. At some point during that visit, my sister said, gently touching a fingertip to her daughter's chin, "I know you're here to do special things, Shelsa. I'll help you in any way I can."

All of us heard her say that and we didn't so much as exchange a look. Seese's comment seemed to fall somewhere in the middle of the spectrum of loving eccentricity where she'd long ago set up her tent. I almost forgot it. But then, on the flight home, after spending some time looking out the window to her left, Jeannie turned to me and said, "I've seen a lot of babies in my time, Hon, you know. But there did seem to be something unusual about Shelsa."

"In what way?"

Jeannie shrugged her slim shoulders, a gesture I'd seen a thousand times. It didn't mean she lacked an opinion, or wasn't going to answer the question; it meant she was laying down a sort of napkin of humility upon which to set whatever she planned to say next. A woman of strong opinions, she never stated them as if they were God's truth, or even the words of an expert, and that was one of the many things I loved about her. She glanced out at the clouds again, then turned back to me and said, so quietly that the kids, sitting behind us, couldn't hear, "She never cried, did you notice? I've never seen a healthy baby that didn't cry. When she was hungry or needed to be changed, she just looked at her mother a certain way, as if Cecelia was supposed to know. It gave me goose bumps."

"I didn't notice," I said. "I'm not that much of a baby expert," and I filed Jeannie's observation away.

On later visits, however, when Seese, Rinpoche, and Shelsa came east, or, more often, when we met them someplace out west, I did start to pay more attention to Shelsa's behavior, and it did begin to seem at least somewhat unusual. She learned to talk very early—at eight months—and to walk not long afterwards. As a toddler, she seemed to seek out her father wherever he went, often finding him in meditation, sitting down next to him, and closing her eyes. That wasn't so strange. Lots of kids imitate their mom and dad. But when she was four, Shelsa behaved like a typical six-year-old, and when she was six, like an eight-year-old (she read all the Harry Potter books before she was out of kindergarten and could recite verbatim long sections of the complicated Tibetan chants she'd heard her dad sing.) Anthony loved her, but it was Natasha who noticed the unusual aspects. "Shelsa understands the cycle of the moon, Dad," she told me once. "She's eight. She explained it all to me and she said it's connected to our spiritual evolution, that some 'fully realized people'—that was the term she used!—die on or near the full moon. And also that sometimes a shimmering rainbow forms around them for a few seconds after they stop breathing! It's a little spooky."

I reserved judgment. Withholding my opinion or making pleasant, neutral comments has always been a specialty of mine, though that's not something I'm particularly proud of. The habit comes, I think, from the growing distance I felt as an adolescent from the ethos of the North Dakota farm culture. I couldn't say what I really felt about that way of life, not in front of my parents. I couldn't express my discomfort with the religion of taciturnity, with the insistence upon order above all else, as if the roads, laid out in grids as they were, and the neat straight lines of corn, wheat, and beans, were symbols, not only of the right way to be in this world, but the *only* way to be. And then, years later, sitting around a conference table in the Manhattan publishing house of Stanley and Byrnes, moving slowly up the ladder from Administrative Assistant, to Associate Editor, to Travel Editor, to Senior Editor, taking my cues from older executives, I'd learned to keep the strongest feelings to myself, to dilute my commentary, to say things like, "I think there's some merit to this proposal," rather than, "I love this!" Jeannie would sometimes chide me about it. "Don't be afraid to tell the kids in blunt terms what you really think, Otto," she'd say. "Positive and negative. They need that from you."

"I'm a North Dakotan," I'd say. "We don't have positive and negative. We have not so good and pretty good and not bad."

And so on.

For years, as Shelsa grew, I watched her and reserved comment, but as time went on I began to see, in my black-haired niece who'd been born to my blond-haired sister, what I saw in Rinpoche: a perfect ordinariness on the one hand, and, on the other, moments that opened into some other dimension, something human, of course, but also unlike any human I knew. Here's an example: One time when we were visiting, Shelsa said, in the middle of supper, "Phone," and three seconds later the phone rang. What word do you give to something like that without venturing into the vocabulary of the roadside psychics?

"Special" was Seese's word of choice, but she sent her daughter to public school and made her do chores around the farm, and told me Shelsa had to navigate the usual challenges with friends and studies.

Here's another of my bad habits: too often, instead of dealing with uncomfortable subjects or situations, I wait for them to go away. I was uneasy with my sister's comments about

Shelsa, and quietly uneasy with my family's general agreement that there was, in fact, something *special* about her. And so, naturally, I hoped that, as she grew toward adolescence, Shelsa's unusual aspects would fade and she'd turn into a good, solid, attractive, intelligent, ordinary American girl.

How foolish of me.

One night, some years after Jeannie's death, not long after Shelsa turned eleven, Seese called me at home. "Otto, my dear brother," she began, and that was the signal: I was in trouble. "Otto, Ila Rinpoche was right! We've had confirming reports now! There's a child in Italy. In the mountains. A boy. He's the partner for Shelsa, the one we've been expecting!"

"We have?"

I heard her click her tongue against her teeth, her favorite expression of disdain since adolescence. "I've told you about this, haven't I?"

"I was there, Seese. Four years ago in Vegas with Ila Rinpoche and Natasha and Rinp, remember?"

"You're sure?"

"Absolutely. I remember them saying the child had been born, Shelsa's partner in crime."

"Not crime, Otto!"

"It's an expression, I—"

"Well, anyway, it's for sure now. We're going to have to go over there to get them together. Rinpoche wants you to come, and so do I. And we have to go by boat because, you know, Rinpoche doesn't like to fly. I've made reservations for us on the Queen Mary. Anthony and Natasha can come—I got all of us tickets for the first crossing of the summer, just after Anthony gets finished with school. I'll send you the exact details. I wrote them down somewhere, but I can't find the piece of paper."

Thirteen

My sister did find the piece of paper, and we did, in fact, cross the Atlantic on the Queen Mary II that summer and spend time in Italy—Seese, Rinpoche, Shelsa, my daughter Natasha, and I (Anthony had football camp). It would turn out to be a bizarre family vacation, one that sent tremors through the very foundation of what I believed possible on this earth.

To begin with—and this would be a sort of evil precursor to the 2022 'trouble' Rinp mentioned at the coffeeshop near Revere Beach—shortly before we left, Shelsa received an ominous threat. Truer to say, Seese received it, via the old-fashioned heavy black telephone that had sat on a side table in the kitchen of our North Dakota farmhouse for decades without ever transmitting a word of hatred. A man's voice: "Death to the little heretic." That was all.

That was enough. At my urging, then my insistence, Seese reported it to the local police, who relayed it to the FBI. An agent was sent to interview the family. Ultimately, nothing came of it, nothing physical, at least, no home invasion, no kidnapping, no gunshots. But, understandably, my sister was deeply shaken and spoke to me by phone every day for two weeks after the threatening call.

To complicate matters, during that time, western North Dakota was undergoing a radical change. Fifty years earlier, oil had been discovered on the property of a farmer named Henry O. Bakken. As the decades passed and measuring instruments grew more sophisticated, geologists discovered that this was no ordinary strike: estimates of the reserves in what came to be known as the "Bakken Field" ranged from three billion to a hundred and fifty billion barrels. An astounding number, at either end of that guess. Oil companies had by then refined their methods of extraction, including the use of a controversial process called "hydraulic fracturing," or "fracking", and by the turn of the millennium, the Bakken Field was producing 450,000 barrels a day. Fracking crews had arrived in droves, and places like Williston, to the north and west of us, had turned into Wild West boomtowns complete with stabbings, imported prostitutes, housing shortages, and rough-looking men packing pistols. People, we heard, were locking their doors for the first time in generations.

Our farm lay to the south and east of the Bakken, near the less-busy city of Dickinson, an area that hadn't been affected as much by the fracking boom. But, Seese told me, all of central and western North Dakota had lost some of its high-plains innocence, and she worried that the phone call was only another chapter in their troubles. A few years earlier, a splash of bizarre, bright red, anti-Muslim graffiti had been spray-painted on one of the farm's retreat cabins. Why anti-Muslim? We guessed that the person who'd sneaked onto the farm and done the deed in darkness didn't know the difference between Buddhism and Islam, or didn't care.

During that flurry of sibling-to-sibling phone calls, Seese talked again of selling the place, setting up Rinpoche's meditation center elsewhere in the lower forty-eight, though, in the end, she, Rinpoche, and Natasha took a vote and unanimously decided to stay. When they'd first heard that Shelsa's so-called 'partner' had been 'incarnated' and would be found in the mountains of Italy, they latched onto the idea with an enthusiasm that was heightened by the local troubles. Time outside the country, they all agreed, might allow for things to quiet down. I wasn't so sure.

Several years passed. For a while, there was no further news of the Italian boy, and Seese stopped mentioning him. But then came these 'confirming reports.' And then the nasty phone call. And then we were off to Italy.

I found our voyage on the Queen Mary II to be an odd experience: bland, gray vistas; opulent, twenty-four-hour buffets; shuffleboard on the top deck; outdoor and indoor swimming pools; a theater; a game room; and one formal dinner at which all of us except the good monk were required to dress up. Compulsive worrier that I am, it seemed to me that the decks, with their chest-high railings formed from thin metal bars, hadn't been built with the safety of children in mind. Whenever we were out in the air with Shelsa, I watched her every second, held her hand firmly when she stood near the railing, told her multiple times not to go outside without Natasha or me or her parents. She was eleven years old, but had always been particularly physically affectionate with me, and didn't seem to mind the hand-holding and my nervous presence.

Everything worked out well—we attended a magic show, we ate, we frolicked in the sloshing waves of the outdoor pool, we played Monopoly in the game room with ocean swells rushing and cresting near the large windows there—until one evening at dinner Shelsa went off to the bathroom alone and didn't return. All week we'd been sharing a table with two women from New Mexico who had some kind of 'super cruiser' status because they made several Cunard trips a year, and we were slightly distracted by a conversation with them about the

Apache reservation where one of them worked. That, a bit too much wine, a succulent strawberry shortcake served with good coffee, and it took us a few minutes longer than it should have to realize that Shelsa hadn't returned.

We immediately set off to find her, Seese heading back to the berths, Tasha to the game room, Rinpoche to the theater and then the shuffleboard court. I went outside and hurried around each of several decks, fast-walking, barely holding a tsunami of panic at bay. She was nowhere to be found.

At last, in desperation, Seese contacted the steward, who arranged for an announcement to be made over the public address system that reached every corner of the huge ship. "If anyone sees an eleven-year-old girl in a white and blue dress wandering around, please bring her to her parents in the main dining area."

We met in the dining area and waited, and waited, my sister clasping my forearm with both hands, Rinpoche working his beads, Natasha in tears. And then the steward came running up to us—literally running—and said, "Found her! Downstairs, come on!"

My darling niece had made her way into the bowels of the great vessel, into one of the staff break rooms, and was sitting there cross-legged on two pillows, imitating her father at one of his talks. But perhaps 'imitating' isn't the right word. A semicircle of servers, room-cleaners, and other assorted employees, probably two dozen in all, were sitting in chairs, or leaning against counters, listening attentively. When she saw us come into the room, Shelsa smiled calmly, and I will always remember her saying, "Here are the ones I love most!"

Neither Rinpoche nor Seese scolded her, not in my presence at least, and most likely not in private. I held my tongue, in part because I'm an uncle, not a father, and in part because something in the atmosphere of the break room made me think the staff had been doing more than humoring her. I was struggling then, as I'd been struggling since the first week of my first road trip with Rinpoche, as I would continue to struggle for years, to strike a balance between a rational skepticism and the kind of open-mindedness Seese and Natasha kept urging me to cultivate.

Next day, out for a couple of loops around the fifth deck, I happened to bump into one of the cleaning women I'd seen in the break room. She was lugging a large plastic bag of just-laundered towels. I held the door for her, walked with her as far as the elevator, and before it arrived, said, "You were with my niece downstairs, weren't you? Last night?"

A smile, a nod, an accented, "I was there."

"What was she saying?"

"She was saying to us about how our thoughts work, how we think in habits, how our mind can go to the same bad place if we let it. She was teaching us to use the meditation to clean our minds."

By then, I'd been at least partially converted to the idea that Shelsa was something other than an ordinary child, but even for me, the idea of her giving a sensible, useful, grown-up-like talk on meditation to the workers on the Queen Mary II was an event that stood on the far side of the believability border. The aforementioned balance was tipping back in the direction of skepticism. I didn't ask Shelsa or Seese or Rinpoche about it. Too afraid, maybe; too worried about what their response might be. But, like the comment Jeannie had made on the plane after our first visit to see our newborn niece, the image of Shelsa talking to a group of rapt Queen Mary workers could not be dislodged from my memory.

The ship docked in Southampton, and we found a smaller boat—a Polish freighter, in fact (the food was excellent!)—to take us to a port city just north of Rome. Civitavecchia, the city was called; we practiced pronouncing it. Chee-veet-ah-VECK-ee-yah. All of us were glad to be on dry land, at last, but none of us—not even Rinpoche or Shelsa—was entirely sure where we should be headed, or what, exactly, we should be doing.

We spent three hot, wonderful days in Rome, seeing the sights. The churches of the Eternal City are, for the most part, left open during the day, and it felt like we visited eighty percent of them. Rinpoche and Shelsa sat quietly in the pews, deep in meditation, while Seese, Natasha, and I meandered the outer aisles marveling at the paintings and sculptures, or sat studying the elaborate marble altars and stained glass windows, or meditated for a few minutes ourselves. On our less spiritual, more touristy outings—to the Coliseum, Pamphili Gardens, Spanish Steps, Piazza del Popolo—Shelsa seemed uncharacteristically distracted, holding to the sleeve of her father's robe with two fingers and knitting her brows as though she were struggling to find the answer to a problem some celestial math teacher had assigned. Rinpoche was happy and upbeat, as always, but I could see that part of his legendary concentration was focused elsewhere, too.

Day by day, as their intuitions were sharpened—apparently by subsequent dreams and visions and the kinds of meditation sessions that were far beyond my reach—our itinerary began to take shape. We moved gradually north, making good use of the Italian train system. We stopped first in the city of Orvieto, a lovely place perched on a geological uplift, an hour north of Rome. Orvieto is known for its white wine—Orvieto Classico—its high-quality ceramics, and its massive Cathedral, *Il Duomo di Orvieto,* the hundred-and-fifty-foot spires of which can be seen from many miles away. Strangely, however, Shelsa wasn't drawn to the cathedral, but to a much smaller and much more modest church a block away, a church so plain that even the most curious traveler might walk past it without a glance. Inside, it seemed old and worn, a few dark paintings on the walls, a relatively simple altar, ten rows of wooden benches, no stained glass. But it was there, after a long, quiet meditation, that Shelsa seemed to have the clearest sense yet of where we might find her partner in prayer. She would tell my sister later that the Italian word for lake—*lago*—had come to her repeatedly, and so we decided to head farther north, toward the lakes district.

The problem was that, as soon as we consulted the map, we realized there are five lakes in that section of the country: Maggiore, Lugano, Garda, Iseo, and Como. And Shelsa didn't know which *lago* was the one where we might find the special boy.

Strangely again, after such a long trip and so much effort, there seemed to be little urgency. We traveled on local trains—twice by bus—and, not far along our northward route, spent the night at one of Rinpoche's meditation centers, a former nunnery called *La Pace*—The Peace—that had been moved from an earlier location near Torino to the city of Montecatini Terme, west of Florence. At the gates of *La Pace,* Rinp was greeted like a movie star. Adults bowed to him and to Shelsa; several people in the crowd of fifty were crying. The famous father and daughter were seated on a stage, and they led a long meditation session, then gave an even longer talk, in English, on the importance of love and compassion. "It's not just a brain exercise," I remember Shelsa saying, in her segment of the talk, which was shorter than her father's. "Meditation shouldn't lead only to quiet. It must lead to caring."

That, from an eleven-year-old.

We were fed a delicious vegetarian dinner, put up in a top-floor section of the ancient building, on beds where nuns had once slept, and sent on our way the next morning with chants and tears, and flowers tossed on the path where Rinpoche and his daughter would walk.

We traveled north, through Modena and Mantova. We visited Lake Garda and Lake Iseo, but only briefly. "Shelsa says these just don't feel like the place," Seese told me. I ate the delicious food, drank the excellent wine, swam with Natasha in the cold water, marveled at Garda's shoreline cliffs and at the crowds of German tourists in Lovere, at Iseo's northern tip.

And I waited, fairly sure that, once we'd seen the last two of the big lakes, the whole search would come to nothing. We'd return home, making excuses about the 'visions.' I'd focus on the vacation aspect of things, how wonderful Italy was, and try not to say anything that might embarrass Rinp, Seese, Natasha, or Shelsa.

We'd been in the country nine days when we arrived on the western shore of Lake Como, and found lodging there in what the Italians call an *agriturismo,* or country inn, high up on the hillside above of the small, pleasant city of Menaggio. I spent most of the first day enjoying the magnificent view across red tile rooftops to the blue lake, and cooling off in the *agriturismo's* swimming pool.

In the afternoon, news broke of the disappearance of the world's two most famous holy men. Everyone reading this will remember that day, when the Pope and Dalai Lama went missing. The holy men weren't found for almost a week, and for those days the world press was full of wild speculation: that they'd been kidnapped and were being held for ransom; that they'd magically risen into heaven or a state of nirvana and would never be seen or heard from again; that they were actually sunbathing on a beach in Sardinia and simply wanted to be left alone. There was no shortage of craziness connected with their disappearance, and no shortage of panic, either.

That night, we strolled downhill to Menaggio for dinner and discovered that the story was on the front page of the evening newspaper, and on TV screens in cafes. The restaurant host and our waiter—everyone, it seemed—had an idea where the holy duo could be found, and an opinion on why they'd disappeared. It never would have occurred to me to think that the Pope and Dalai Lama might be involved in the search that had brought us to Italy. I didn't put them on the same spiritual *level* as my young niece and funny brother-in-law. The two men were acknowledged around the world as spiritual leaders. Shelsa and Rinpoche were spiritual, too, yes, the latter a well-known teacher. But at that meal, when my sister quietly expressed the thought that the Pope and Dalai Lama were, like us, looking for Shelsa's partner, I found the idea absurd, and almost said so.

Next day, after a fine lunch at another local eating spot (spaghetti and clams for me, I remember) someone suggested a hike. We climbed into the hills above Menaggio and, after several hours, came, as if by accident, upon a very old-looking, very secluded house, at the end of a two-lane dirt track. The house had brown stone walls, a turret, a red tile roof, and was half-hidden on three sides by a thick undergrowth of bushes and by mature chestnut trees. The front side, free of foliage, offered a spectacular view down over the lake: blue water, green islands, and the high peaks, hills, and small coastal towns on the far shore.

A few seconds after we spotted the house peeking out from behind the trees and bushes, a small, barefoot, tow-headed boy, three or four years old, appeared in the gravel driveway and waved as if his family had been expecting us for lunch. There was nothing overly excited in his greeting, no surprise at all. Until the boy trotted up to Shelsa and wrapped her in a tight hug for a full minute, it seemed like the most casual of encounters.

The boy—who spoke childish versions of both English and Italian, told us his name was Tomasso and led us along a path between flowering bushes the height of my head. In the house's backyard we were greeted by a stocky, elderly woman who was missing half her teeth. Agnese was her name. Judging by Agnese's greeting—friendly but muted—she, too, seemed to have been expecting us, which was exceedingly strange. An outdoor table, shaded by a chestnut tree and not far from a grape arbor and an old barn, had been set for lunch. For *our* lunch, it turned out—five extra chairs. We were told to take our places, and we enjoyed one of the most delicious lunches I can ever remember eating. The feast began with a salad of blood oranges and slices of fennel in olive oil, then a dish of stewed lentils with bits of tomato mixed in, then a pasta course with a cheesy pesto sauce, then a serving of rabbit stew. Wine, coffee, sweet cream and berries for dessert. I was focused on the food, of course, naturally, but remained at least somewhat aware of the goings-on around me. And strange goings-on they were.

For starters, Shelsa and the little boy sat next to each other and carried on a running conversation—English sprinkled with a few Italian words she seemed to understand—as if they were cousins who saw each other at the beach every summer and were catching up. There was an eerie sense of ease between them, something completely lacking in the usual tentative minutes between children of different ages thrown together in a social setting.

Two minutes after we started in on the first course, a lovely woman stepped out of the stone house and introduced herself as Cinzia, "Though I'm American, and you can call me Cynthia, if you like." Cynthia was in her thirties, with long auburn hair and marble-smooth, tanned skin nearly the color of Rinpoche's medium-brown. She sat at the head of the table, a place that seemed to have been reserved for her, and ran her eyes over the visitors, examining us with what felt like a tender curiosity. Rinpoche was sitting to her right, and after her perusal, she fixed her gaze on him and said, "Many, many people have told me of your wonderful work."

Rinpoche shrugged, as if she were speaking about someone else, then he smiled and said, "You have around you the light."

I ate. Listened. Sometimes lifted my eyes surreptitiously to study Cynthia or Tomasso—who was her son, apparently. At one point, the little boy left his place, hustled over to the head of the table, and planted a loud kiss on his mother's cheek.

I feel I'm not really giving a clear sense of the atmosphere, but the problem is that the atmosphere was at once absolutely normal, and somehow surreal. I felt Natasha staring at me from diagonally across the table, and when I met her gaze, I saw there a more mature version of the same kind of excitement I'd seen when we'd taken a tour of the farm in North Dakota, not long after my sister and I inherited the property and Seese decided to turn it into a meditation center. At the table in Agnese's yard, I could see that Tasha wanted to say something, but was holding the comment for a private moment. Seese was staring at Cynthia, Rinpoche's laugh echoed in the shaded yard, Tomasso and Shelsa had a giggling fit. Agnese kept bringing out food and carrying in empty plates. Natasha and Seese and I all offered to help, but she insisted we remain seated. "I want you love my food," she said in broken English. We assured her that we did.

After the meal, yours truly feeling like a stuffed animal, Tomasso and Shelsa went and sat in front of the house and stared down at the lake, and Cynthia added a cherry to the sundae of the odd afternoon by saying this: "We're in hiding here. My husband died not long ago—he was much older, a former official in the Church—and, I won't go into too much detail, but it seems the birth of Tomasso, such a joy to both my husband and me, caused certain of his former colleagues to be upset. More than upset, in fact. He and Agnese were cousins. He knew we could stay here and have little chance of being bothered."

I asked her if she'd heard the news about the disappearance of the Pope and Dalai Lama and she nodded somberly, started to say something, squeezed her lips together, looked at me as if wondering what kind of person I really was, and then said, "I think we will see them again soon," in a way that might have meant 'see them here in the yard tomorrow' or 'see them alive and well on the TV screen next week'. I nodded politely and kept my mouth closed.

We weren't invited to spend the night; we were told that we must. Cynthia had a tender fierceness about her. Agnese gave us to understand that there was space for all of us in the stone house, Rinpoche, Seese, and Shelsa in one room, and Tasha and I in another. "We have quite a bit of luggage back at the *agriturismo*," I said to Cynthia, "and another few days of reservations there."

"That's fine, Otto. It's not a long walk, is it?"

"Not too long, but—"

"And there's a dirt road not far beyond the barn," she

waved an arm. "It leads up from Sant' Abbondio, the old church near where you're staying. Leave Shelsa here—she'll be fine—and the rest of you can go and retrieve your things and take a cab back. You won't have to pay anything to sleep here, so tell the owners they can keep the payment for your rooms, you're staying with friends. Just please don't tell them exactly where you're going, and tell the cab driver only that you're friends with Agnese."

No one objected, and so I didn't object. From the moment I'd heard Seese talk about sailing to Europe, I'd decided I would go along with the family flow, keep my doubts to myself. Why not? What was the worst that could happen: we'd have an enjoyable family trip that did not include the discovery of Shelsa's spiritual partner? And now that it seemed we'd actually come upon a somewhat mysterious young boy and his mother, if not the other half of my niece's destiny, what was the point in being the only one in the family to resist the flow of events?

Natasha volunteered to walk back with me, so I wouldn't have to handle all the luggage on my own. On the way down the hill, I was half-hoping she'd say something like, "You're being great about all this, Dad. You've been great the whole trip." But, after we'd managed the steepest part of the downhill in silence, what she actually said was, "You understand what's happening, right, Dad?"

I sensed an impending confrontation with my beloved daughter, so I pretended not to hear. She was a step behind me. I was focusing intently on the path—which was rocky and uneven, if no longer particularly steep.

"Dad?"

"What, Hon?"

"You understand what's going on, right?"

"Sure," I said over my shoulder. "We're going to switch lodging and stay up there on the hill. Works fine for me. That was one of the most amazing meals I ever had!"

But I couldn't get away with it. Natasha caught up to me, put a hand on my left arm and made me stop and look at her. "You realize that what Aunt Seese said is true, don't you? That the Pope and the Dalai Lama are most likely looking for Shelsa and Tomasso?"

"Who on earth gave you that idea, Hon?"

"Aunt Seese. You heard her. It makes perfect sense, too, don't you see it?"

At that point, rather suddenly, I lost the ability to pretend, to remain silent, to hold back the enormous cold lake of doubt that had been damming up in my thoughts from the moment Seese pronounced the words, "Queen Mary." What I said was "No, I don't see it!" much, much more forcefully than I intended. I saw smaller lakes accumulate in my daughter's eyes—one of the very worst feelings on this earth. "I'm sorry," I added, almost immediately. "I'm sorry, Tash. I've been trying, really I have. I have no idea why the Pope and Dalai Lama are missing, but the idea that they should have sneaked away from a Vatican summit in the hope of finding two . . . *children,* it's just too much. I've tried to be polite about it. I've tried not to say anything. What I think, what I really think, is that Shelsa is a very, very smart young girl, special in many ways. And Tomasso is a cute little boy. It's not the first time a young girl and a little boy made a connection and liked to play with each other. I've been alive so much longer than you have, Hon, and I respect your intelligence absolutely, but I think everybody except me is under a kind of spell cast by your lovely aunt, who's been imagining weird scenarios since about three months after she learned to talk. I'm sorry, really. I'm sorry I yelled. I'm just, I don't know, massively frustrated, that's all. I can't pretend anymore, not with you."

"And Cynthia?" Natasha said calmly, after one swipe across her eyes.

"A very attractive, calm woman. A loving mother."

"Yeah, okay. But she . . . I don't know, she . . . you've heard the expression 'divine feminine,' right?"

"I have."

"Well, she, like, *embodies* it. Did you notice the way she and Rinpoche were looking at each other? It was like they were brother and sister or something. I even thought Aunt Seese was a little jealous."

"I can't picture her being jealous."

"And Shelsa and Tomasso. It's so weird the way they took to each other. Even the older woman, Agnese, she, I don't know, she has a certain *grace* about her, and she served Cynthia as if she were serving a queen."

"I missed that. I'm sorry."

Tasha looked at me with an even mix of love and pity. "Do you know who Cynthia's husband was?"

"I haven't the faintest idea."

"Agnese told me in the kitchen that he was the former Cardinal of Genoa, hugely respected in the Church."

"And he left the Church to get married to a very attractive woman. Hardly a first."

I was ready to move on, downhill. Tasha wasn't. She held me there with her eyes, her patience, her love. "Do you believe at all in what people call miracles, Dad?" she said. "I mean, not just the ones in the Bible, but in general. Do you believe things like that happen? Things we can't explain?"

I shrugged. "I don't know. I don't think so. Not anymore. I prayed so hard for a miracle that would keep your mother alive, and . . . and it didn't work out. Obviously. Let's keep walking, okay? We still have to get back to the *agriturismo* and talk to Enrico about leaving and collect the bags and call a cab and everything. Your uncle and aunt will think we got lost, or mugged, or something."

"Sure, Dad," she said, holding me in her gaze for a few more seconds. "It's good to worry about the practical stuff, but I just wonder what it will take to make you let go of the last part of the New York corporate cynicism, and really see what's going on."

"I love you. I love Aunt Seese and Rinp and Shelsa. There's nothing cynical about that."

"I know, Dad. And we love you back, me more than anyone. But didn't you see the way Mom was near the very end, when the pain was finally gone?"

"I did. I saw peace. I was grateful for that. She opened her eyes and looked at us one at a time and I saw peace there. And love. She lived a few more hours and—"

"I saw *understanding*. I think you did, too."

"Of?"

My daughter shrugged, looked away, down across the treetops to the magnificent lake. "Of something beyond," she swung an arm to encompass the view, "this. I think Aunt Seese sees it, but maybe she just has glimpses, and they get mixed up with her personality, which has a whacky side."

"I'm glad you—"

"I think Rinpoche sees it all the time. Like, constantly. It's why he's so goofy sometimes, because he sees that everything we think is real is only, I don't know, *partly* real. There's some other *real* for him, something bigger. What Mom saw at the end, Rinpoche *lives*, Dad. *Lives*. And Shelsa inherited that. If you spent more time with her, you'd see it, too. I know you would.

And I think Tomasso lives it, too, though he's so young it's easy to dismiss it all, and see him as just another cute little kid."

I nodded, half-convinced, trying as hard as I could to sweep my skepticism aside. Tasha smiled, sadly. I hugged my wonderful daughter and held her for a few seconds, an apology. We walked on then. Down to the beautiful *agriturismo,* with the beautiful view, and the beautiful pool. We collected our luggage there, asked Enrico, the somewhat offended owner ("You didn't enjoy the rooms?"), to call us a cab, and endured a bumpy ride with a sullen driver who asked no questions. We spent three pleasant days in the stone house, eating Agnese's delicious meals, taking hikes, and watching Shelsa and Tomasso enjoy each other's company.

And then, on the fourth day, the Pope and the Dalai Lama showed up and joined us.

Fourteen

On that fourth day near Lake Como, after an outdoor breakfast, Rinpoche, Seese, Tasha, Shelsa, and I borrowed a scuffed-up soccer ball we found in Agnese's yard and wandered down to a local field, hoping to get some exercise. In an attempt to devote myself more seriously to the meditative life, I'd been keeping my hair very short, almost a complete shave, and I remember I had to put sun screen on my scalp before we left Agnese's house. Tomasso, Cynthia, and Agnese stayed home, but before we left I noticed that a small extension had been connected to the end of the table where we'd been eating, and four new places set there. More visitors, I supposed, and I braced myself for the next dimension of oddness.

The day was hot, but a brisk cool breeze softened the heat, and the five of us enjoyed a fine half hour of kicking the ball around and taking turns playing goalie. Rinpoche almost made a save on a hard shot by Tasha, and then, laughing, retrieved the ball from the net and gave it a ferocious kick, the cloth of his robe lifting up to reveal his underwear, and the ball arcing up and over our heads and bounding toward one corner of the far end of the field. It was only when Shelsa trotted away to retrieve it that I noticed we weren't alone. Four other amateur soccer players, a woman and three men, were horsing around at the other goal. Shelsa trotted toward the corner at first, and then stopped, changed direction, walked up to one of the strangers, and bowed.

105

When she made no effort to retrieve the ball and return to us, we all followed her to that end of the field. Another minute or so of more or less ordinary, sane, predictable life and then I learned that the stranger to whom Shelsa had bowed was the Dalai Lama . . . disguised, and I will swear to this, as a kind of Mediterranean jet-setter. His playing partners—also sporting rather bizarre disguises—included the Pope and the two accomplices who'd arranged for the holy men's escape. Seese immediately realized that she'd been correct: the Pope and Dalai Lama, prompted by mysterious signs, had come in search of Tomasso and Shelsa. I know this because she gave me one of her famous *'See, Otto! What did I tell you?!'* looks. Once we were introduced and once I had, very slowly, swallowed my pride and regained my ability to speak, it seemed only natural to head back to Agnese's house and bring Tomasso into the circus.

What happened over the next twenty hours was, I have to admit, strangely unremarkable, almost ordinary, given the people involved. Agnese served us another fantastic meal. The odd couple, husband and wife, who'd enabled the escape of the two holy men, told us the story of the journey they'd just made, north from Rome, knowing all the while that the world was looking for them. A huge reward had been offered for information leading to the kidnappers' arrest and the Pope and Dalai Lama's safe return. We were told that the holy men had, at first, simply wanted to take a sort of vacation, to shed their celebrity status for a bit. But then they'd started having dreams, and realized that the dreams were leading them to a special child, or children.

While I ate, listened, and observed, I was engaged in a furious interior battle with both my pride and my skepticism. The conversation around the long table in that peaceful back yard made it perfectly clear that my sister had been correct, and that Tasha had been correct in believing her: Shelsa and Tomasso were, in fact, destined to meet. The Pope and Dalai Lama had, in fact, sensed their presence in Italy. Cynthia did, in fact, exhibit a sort of divinity, for lack of a better word. That much was undeniable. What bolstered the less open-minded side of my interior battlefield was the fact that, once all these people found each other, absolutely nothing remarkable happened. There were no miracles. No one levitated. No voices spoke to us from the blue Italian sky. The Pope, Dalai Lama, Agnese, Cynthia, and the Italian couple engaged in a lively, multi-lingual conversation with Rinpoche and my sister; the two special children laughed at private jokes, hugged each other, and sat out in the front yard looking down at the lake. We ate a long, leisurely lunch, and then an even longer dinner out in Agnese's shaded back yard. Some of us drank copious amounts of wine. But that was basically all that happened.

After the lengthy dinner, my family and I, Shelsa at the lead, accompanied little Tomasso into the stone house and sang him to sleep. We spent the night there—the elegant Italian couple (who seemed to have once been married) out in the barn, yours truly tossing and turning in a tiny attic room—and then, very early the next morning, since the car they'd used in their escape had been discovered where they left it, in Menaggio, and since Cynthia did not want attention called to her son, the Pope and Dalai Lama and the couple of 'kidnappers' walked into the town and turned themselves in.

Like most such spectacular stories, the holy men's trip conquered the media for a week or so and then was more or less overtaken by fresher news. A year later, those two elegant accomplices—the Pope's cousin and his Italian wife, Paolo and Rosa were their names and they had, in fact, been separated and reconciled—published a book about the clandestine adventure, *The Delight of Being Ordinary*. The title referred to the desire on the part of both holy men to shed their fame for a short while and try to experience life as ordinary human beings, and that was the main theme of the story.

Somewhat to my embarrassment, however, Rinpoche and Seese and Shelsa and Natasha and I had a cameo role in that book, appearing in a couple of chapters near the end. Fortunately for us, it was a full year before the book was published, so our role was never made public in the news reports, and, once things quieted down a bit, the five of us had been able to slip away from Agnese's house, spend a few more days in Italy, and return home without publicity. We have maintained a steady but irregular contact with Cynthia and Tomasso to this day.

The Delight of Being Ordinary—fairly well written and apparently truthful—gives a more detailed description of the curious events, so I won't alienate my own readers any further here by dwelling on our Italian adventure, except to say what I've said before: my commitment is to the truth, and, in reporting this part of the story, I have tried to be as honest as possible. Did it alter my view of my sister's so-called visions and predictions? Yes, but only to a point. A long-term skepticism still had its claws in me, and it argued that, in the end, beside the strange encounters and the arrival of the holy men, nothing otherworldly had actually occurred. In my eyes, Shelsa and Tomasso were still just kids. Here's a footnote: as the blessed Catholic-Buddhist entourage was heading out of the yard on that final morning, little Tomasso ran up behind Paolo, the Pope's cousin, and kicked him in the calf—not exactly what you'd expect from a young saint-in-waiting.

Fifteen

The yellow station wagon, with the "GOD BLESS EVERY-
ONE, NO EXCEPTIONS!" bumper sticker, was still one car-
length ahead of us in the next lane when my overactive
mind returned from its Italian musings. By then, we were in
the southernmost part of The Garden State, and I realized I
had to make a decision about which route to choose.

I should say here that I have absolutely nothing against Baltimore; I simply do not like driving through that city on the Interstate. Despite the troubles it shares with every other large
American city, I'm sure many Baltimoreons (that is the correct
term) consider it a perfectly fine place to live, and I admit to
having spent five pleasant days there at two different book
fairs. I just find the through-driving difficult, the array of tunnels and bridges confusing and vaguely disheartening, and so,
over the years, whenever I traveled to the nation's capital, taking the kids to see the White House and the museums and so
on, I fell into the habit of choosing an alternate route. So, after
Rinpoche and I traveled down the New Jersey Turnpike for a
while, I left the superhighway for Route 301, which led us into
the flat farmland of northern Delaware, and enabled us to skip
Baltimore entirely.

Perhaps sensing the change in speed, Rinpoche opened his
eyes.

"You hungry, Rinp? Need to stop to pee?"

"Yes to the one and no to the two."

"Any particular kind of food?"

"What the kind you want, Otto."

I took the next promising-looking exit and swept in a big loop to the east and down onto a straight, mid-size divided highway with what appeared to be a mall of some sort ahead of us on the left. I'd turned on the radio by then, and caught the latest news from Ukraine. Russians shelling civilian targets, millions fleeing to Poland, Romania, and other countries, women giving birth in subway stations and bomb shelters, children being killed. I couldn't stop thinking about the horror of it all, and didn't want to stop thinking about it, didn't want to ignore that suffering and just go about my happy business. I'd sent money to a Ukrainian relief organization. Seese and Rinp and Natasha and I had put our names on a list to host refugees, if they were able to come all the way to North Dakota and wanted to live in a place so remote. There was nothing else I could do, I knew that, but, at the same time, I didn't want to turn my mind and heart away from what was happening in Kharkiv and Donetsk. I'd felt that way during the civil war in Syria, too—more hell on earth. Jeannie and I had long been members of Amnesty International, had always tried to ease suffering where we could. We enjoyed our own lives, of course, and tried to give the kids a happy childhood, but we always made sure, in the midst of our luxury, to keep a quiet little room in the back of our minds as a shrine to others' grief.

"You bought a beautiful truck, Rinp," I said, to chase away the war images. "Great gas mileage and it feels like you're floating, the ride is so smooth."

Rinpoche nodded and grunted and I could tell by the small smile on his face that he was pleased. "We giving it away," he said. "After."

"Really?"

"Sure."

"Giving it away to an organization? A charity?"

"To Les."

"Les Ingler? Your whacky neighbor?"

"What means?"

"Whacky? It means loopy, nutty, odd, eccentric."

Another grunt. "Les has the truck all with rusty and broken sometimes. Doesn't have money for the new one."

If he'd pay attention to his crops, or get a job instead of playing cards, and watching reality TV and the horse races all the time, he might have enough money for a new truck was the beautiful thought that danced across my inner stage at that moment. But, of course, that thought wasn't beautiful at all. I'd long ago put Les Ingler in a box, slapped the label *whack-job* on the box, and set it in a corner. Unfair of me, no doubt. Still, I felt a tickle of bother at the idea of lazy, crazy Les getting a brand new truck without having to work for it, and I couldn't understand why Rinpoche would make such a peculiar gift. I'd thought he'd purchased the pickup for his own use around the farm, for one thing. And, for another, if he were determined to give it away, there were organizations that deserved it more than Les Ingler.

By the time I'd managed to set aside these thoughts, we were abreast of the mall, one of those gleaming arrangements of chain shops and restaurants set along three sides of a huge, newly paved parking lot. You see such places everywhere near the Interstates, at least along the Eastern Seaboard. The food offerings aren't usually very good, but there's an abundance of parking, and these roadside shopping spots offer the convenience of being able to buy your shaving gear at a CVS, your reading glasses at a Dollar Tree, and then grab an artery-choking cheeseburger at Burger King, all within a few steps of

111

your vehicle. They're easy and safe and clean, but I was in a critical mood and knew that, in small city after small town all up and down the coast and all across the lower forty-eight, these shrines to convenience had sucked the life out of the old commercial centers. Jeannie was always particularly upset by that. When the kids were in grammar and middle school, we'd sometimes drive south for their spring break, heading down I-95 to South Carolina, Georgia, or Florida, to get out of the raw New York weather and have a week or two together on the road. Rather than risk rest-stop food, we'd always pull off the highway for our meals, and inevitably end up in some Frontville or West Dinton where half or two-thirds of the storefronts were empty, the local cinema long closed, an ancient, family-owned furniture or jewelry store clinging to life by its fingernails, and an elderly couple emerging on walkers from the one functioning cafe. "These places are the heart and soul and lungs and liver and kidneys of America," Jeannie said to me once, in one of those places. I remember that moment so well. The kids had gone off to the rest rooms, and she and I were sitting across from each other in a booth with torn red leatherette seats. "And it looks like they've been eaten away by some kind of cancer. It makes me so sad."

"It's just the system," I said. "The Mom and Pop places can't compete with the big chains, because the big chains buy things in bulk and can survive if each of a thousand outlets makes only a few hundred dollars a week. And there's not enough parking in the old downtowns. It's just the system, that's all, just math, profit, speed, convenience."

"Then the system has no soul," she said, "and it's ugly, too." The kids were making their noisy return then, and they were young, so Jeannie and I set the subject aside and turned the conversation toward happier fields.

In this particular mall, however, amid the farmland of northern Delaware, I spotted a Japanese restaurant that didn't seem to be part of a national chain. I parked right in front, and Rinpoche and I stepped inside.

The place was clean and new, black tabletops, prints of Mt. Fuji on the walls, the waitress young and petite and so shy she seemed to require a few seconds to build up her courage before she approached the table, handed us menus, and asked what we wanted to drink. Hot green tea, ice water. When she returned, I ordered a Bento box with beef, rice, and dumplings, and my traveling partner went with one of their more exotic rolls: spicy tuna with small slabs of avocado on top, dribbled with a special sauce.

"Rinp," I admitted, when we were partway through the meal. "I can't stop thinking about the war in Ukraine."

"Wery bad, Otto," he said. "Awfulable thing."

"I wonder what I'd do, how I'd behave. I wonder if it's ever spiritually justified to use violence. In a situation like that, I mean."

He sipped from his mug of tea and fixed his eyes on me. "You makin' a question?" he said.

"Yes."

Another sip. I noticed for the first time that the muscles of his powerful neck had sagged slightly, and that the fine film of hair on his shaved head was now more gray than brown. Rinpoche was somewhere in his seventies, Seese thought. Late or early seventies, even she didn't know. He'd always seemed ageless to me, and now I realized that time had touched even my vibrant brother-in-law. It frightened me, I have to say, foolish as that sounds.

"Hard question," he said.

"One of the big ones."

He smiled. There was one roll left on his plate, and, after offering it to me, he spent a few seconds moving it this way and that with his chopsticks, then suddenly took hold of it, plopped it into his mouth and chewed thoughtfully, gratefully. A swallow, another sip of tea, the clear brown eyes on me again. "I think maybe sometimes you have to."

"Use violence, you mean."

"Maybe. Not sure. For Buddha maybe, for the Jesus, the Mary, maybe not. The Gandhi. The King Martin. Maybe not. But for the people like us," he swung an arm around as if to encompass the nearly empty restaurant and the entire world of ordinary folk, "sometimes maybe you have to take to yourself the heavy karma to protect the other people from, you know, the Putin and them."

"A few years ago, when Anthony was in college, you two used to wrestle."

The big smile appeared. "Too old now," he said. "Probably."

"Right, but Anthony was in great shape, and strong. A linebacker on the football team. And every single time, you'd have him on the ground on his back in about five seconds."

More smiling. Rinpoche had very faint eyebrows—he was, in general, not a hairy man—but when he raised and lowered them, as he did just then, the two fine strips of hair seemed almost able to speak. "Fun," he said.

"Right, but where did you learn that? I never asked you. It looked like some kind of martial arts. Did you take classes or something?"

"My father teach me."

"Does it have a name? Karate? Kung Fu? Tai Chi?"

"He had a name for it, my father." Rinpoche spread out the fingers of his left hand and pressed them not-quite-flat against the tabletop. "What do you call the bottom of the tree. Under the ground part? I forget."

"Root?"

"Yes. Energy of the root, he calls it, my father. He showed me from the time I was very small, Otto. We used to wessle in the yard. My mother, very sweet person, never angry, didn't like to seeing it."

"Serious wrestling?"

"Sure. In the start, he could win every time, didn't try. Later, he tried and still was winning every time. Then, later, sometimes I win. Then they took him to jail."

"The Russians."

"Yes."

"For his spiritual teaching."

"Yes, Otto. Told you before."

"And he died there?"

Rinpoche shook his head. "He came home to die. They let him. Wery strong still, but he was ready to die and he told them and they knew who he was and they let him come home."

"How old was he?"

A big shrug. "Nobody knew it. Not too old as me, maybe."

"They just let him go?"

"They knew he was the master. He told me the men didn't like to keep him there, but they have to. The bosses told them they have to and sometimes they beated him."

"Did you ever see him fight another person?"

Rinpoche laughed and shook his head. "Didn't need to fight, Otto, my father. Never."

"But he taught you?"

"Sure. Not to fight, just to use the energy, that's all. I try to show Anthony, but he didn't want it."

"We'll see him in a few days."

"Good, good," Rinpoche said, and then he mangled yet another one of the expressions he'd heard from Les Ingler, or from my sister. "Couldn't wait," he said. "Couldn't wait to see him!"

Sixteen

I tipped the shy waitress eight times the cost of our meal and went outside all ready to get back on the highway and drive toward D.C. so we could beat the rush-hour traffic. I was imagining that part of the route, in fact. Solving, in advance, a problem that had not yet arisen. Behind the wheel of the marvelous truck, I'd pulled out of the mall parking lot and, buried in that imagined future, was heading for the on-ramp when Rinpoche said, "Go in, Otto."

"In where?"

"The hatchets place! You go in here. I saw it."

On our right, just before the ramp that led back toward Route 301, I spotted the mouth of a long, curling dirt driveway. I turned there and, two hundred yards ahead, noticed a windowless box of a building with STUMPY'S HATCHET HOUSE painted in large letters on one side. I hadn't noticed it on the drive toward the mall, but the word 'hatchet' did ring a certain small bell. My son Anthony was working in Charlotte, North Carolina—Rinpoche and I hoped to visit him on this trip—and, from the information he passed on during our infrequent phone conversations, he was enjoying an active social life. Much of that social life was familiar to me: enjoyable dates, late nights at bars with friends and co-workers, restaurant meals, scoring courtside tickets to the games of Charlotte's professional basketball franchise, the Hornets. Once or twice Anthony mentioned he'd gone out with a group of friends to

117

'throw some hatchets'. I'd asked him about it. He'd provided a few details. And I'd set it aside until the moment I saw the large letters on the side of Stumpy's.

There were three other cars in the gravel lot. Inside, the decor was a cross between hunting lodge and warehouse, with rough-sawn beams and what appeared to be a series of large cages, open in front, with wire side walls and wooden targets opposite the open end. After a friendly greeting at the desk, Rinpoche and I were directed over to two of the several small screens set up at waist height. There, we were required to fill out online forms that asked for every single piece of information that described a modern person, with the exception of the sacred Social Security number. Name, address, phone, email, reason for coming to Stumpy's (one box that could be checked read "Hatchet Therapy"). Partly because I had to help Rinpoche with this task, and partly because I'm constitutionally averse to filling out any kind of form, it seemed to me that I was being asked to give height, weight, history of sexual activity, preferred color of crayon, favorite food, number of crowns and implants, upper and lower, if applicable, and my waist size both presently and when I'd been a junior in college. It then seemed that I had to agree to a lengthy description of all the horrible things that might happen during hatchet therapy—losing limbs, giving a spouse reason for divorce, shingles, diverticulitis, blurred vision, the development of sudden bivalve allergies.

Of course, none of that was true, but it felt that way as we stood in front of the screens. Forms frustrate me. Online forms frustrate me to the fifth power and baffle Rinpoche utterly. I don't know what it is, but 'form-resistance' is a longstanding ailment of mine, one that became a family joke when Jeannie was alive. I think it has something to do with the lack of precision. Some questions—address, for example—are straightforward enough. But much of the time the answer needs an explanation, and there isn't room for an explanation. You either fit neatly into this category or that one. There's no middle ground. For instance: *Reason for wanting to throw hatchets.* There was no box for *Because my son had done it a few times and my brother-in-law seemed excited about it.* And I wasn't about to check *hatchet therapy.*

In any case, after signing the document that assured the owners of Stumpy's that, if we sliced ourselves up with one of their hatchets, we wouldn't hold them liable, Rinp and I went back to the desk, paid the fee ($25 per person, per hour) and were led to one of the alleys, or chambers, or booths, or whatever is the proper term. Near us at belt-level stood a small wooden box, divided into two parts and holding two hatchets. If it hadn't been for the abundance and variety of beers for sale near the relaxing area, it would have been hard to imagine how any sane, sober, reasonable person might actually face any danger there at Stumpy's.

A tall, convivial young man named Mason met us at our cage and offered some brief instruction. You could, it turned out, throw with one hand or two. You shouldn't throw while the other person was retrieving his hatchet. You shouldn't try to flip the weapon, but simply release the handle as your arm moved forward above your shoulder. "Most people take about ten minutes to get the hatchet to stick," Mason said. "And then you'll be all set."

Rinpoche got the hatchet to stick on the first throw, and made a bull's eye, too. There was a large bell hanging to one side of the cage, and a sign saying you should pull the rope and ring the bell for every bull's eye. I rang the bell. I then threw the hatchet, which bounced helplessly off the scarred wooden target and lay on its side on the floor, mocking me. As Rinpoche watched, I retrieved it. Threw again. Another bounce. I repeated this eleven times.

Eleven. I counted.

Between my throws, Rinpoche took a few turns on his side of the cage. His hatchet stuck in the wall each time, though only about half the time in the target's black center. In the booth near ours, in lieu of the loud bell-ringing, two young women would kiss and briefly make out every time one of them scored a bull's eye. I was happy for them, happy for Rinpoche, happy for Mason and all the other people on earth who could throw a hatchet the way it should be thrown. When I wasn't banging the hatchet against the wall, I rang the bell for my brother-in-law's successes. And rang it. And rang it so often that, eventually, Mason noticed and came over with a big smile on his face. "You've done this before, man!" he said to Rinpoche.

Rinpoche smiled back at him and shook his head, no.

"Come on, no lyin' here. You're like a pro! And I like the outfit!"

"Never tried it before this time," Rinpoche said.

Mason, clearly not a believer, gave me a quick lesson, told me to stand a foot closer and throw harder, and I did, then, finally, manage to get the hatchet to stick in the wall. One time. Followed by seven straight misses. By then, two of the other throwing booths were occupied, bells were ringing everywhere, and I was coming to better understand the idea of hatchet therapy. If you weren't angry about something when you arrived and signed away your life, you'd certainly be angry after twenty or thirty tries to get the hatchet to stick in a wall so close in front of you that, had you been contagious, you could have infected it with a strong sneeze. I'm not a particularly uncoordinated person. I played hockey in college, was renowned among my friends there for my dart-throwing prowess, played a decent game of tennis well into middle age. But, even with two more instructional visits from the smiling Mason, I simply could not get the accursed blade to lodge itself in the wall. To make matters worse, Rinpoche started throwing with his left hand. He missed once, and then stuck the blade four times in a row, though never in the bull's eye. He did this without any sense of boasting or gloating, easily, naturally, the way Michael Jordan might make free throws in practice. Swish. Swish. I found myself trying to remember the few things Rinpoche *wasn't* good at: golf was one, according to a report from Anthony, who'd played a few rounds with his uncle. Bowling, another. The more I missed, the angrier I became, and the angrier I became, the harder I threw. And the harder I threw, the farther the hatchet bounced away from the wall, at times doing a little crooked dance of derision, handle-to-blade-to-handle, on the rubber carpeting at that end of the booth.

Finally, I gave up. The women to our left were engaged in a very long, passionate kiss (how I missed kissing my wife!), thanks, perhaps, to double bull's eyes. I was happy for them. Rinpoche seemed to have fallen into a meditative trance and was tossing his hatchet so easily, alternating hands, that the folds of his robe barely moved. Mason came over again, but as soon as he started to make suggestions, I stopped him. "Thanks, I'm all set."

"Lots of people have trouble at first. You'll get it. Just—"

"I don't want to get it," I said, perhaps harshly. Mason's smile dimmed. "It's great," I said. "Lots of fun. My brother-in-law is a natural, but it's just, you know . . . not my thing."

Mason relented at last. I was tempted to go back to the front desk and order a beer, but, my parents having been killed by a drunk driver, I usually keep to a strict rule about not drinking when I drive. So there was no escape. It took a few more throws, but Rinpoche finally seemed to sense my *agita*. He picked up both hatchets in one hand and dropped them together into the holding box, wrapped his other arm around me and squeezed me hard against him. "Doesn't make you a bad person," was all he said. We thanked the woman at the front desk, passed through a small group in the lounge area, men and women about my age who were chatting excitedly about some kind of bull's eye competition they were arranging for themselves, and we were out in the air again.

Rinpoche climbed into the passenger seat, but I told him I needed a moment, and I stood out in the parking lot for a spell, gazing across a flat, fallow field, breathing. These were my thoughts: *All these years of meditation. All this time with one of the great spiritual teachers on earth. Retreats. Reading. Prayers. Fasting. Even kept your head shaved for a while. Everything you've been through in life. And you let something like THIS upset you!!*

I breathed. Made circles with my right wrist, my throwing wrist, which seemed to have been mildly sprained on one of the later, angrier, tosses. Perhaps, I thought, I could file suit. Engage one of the lawyers that were advertising everywhere in those days. Obtain a large settlement for damages to my writing hand. Use the money to start my own hatchet house in North Dakota, and bring joy to other people there.

By the time I'd stood out in the air for two minutes, breathing and thinking absurd thoughts, I'd regained a degree of perspective. Maybe that was the reward for all those years of meditation: not that I didn't behave foolishly. Not that I didn't get upset over trivial things. But that it didn't take me too long to regain my balance, such as it was. The hatchet debacle would remain in my thoughts for months afterwards, but the pain of it would shrink with time, resurfacing only in my clumsiest hours, and whenever I happened to read or hear the H-word.

Seventeen

During the hour and a half it took us to reach the outskirts of Washington, Rinpoche remained quiet. Seese had arranged for us to stay at a Hyatt Regency in Bethesda, one of the more expensive hotels in one of the Capital's pricier suburbs, and she'd hinted there would be a meeting with one of Rinpoche's numberless friends. "No eating tonight," Rinpoche said as we checked in. "Meditate, sleep. Okay, Otto?"

"Sure," I said. The woman at the desk handed back my credit card and license. "We were hatching-throwing," I said to her for absolutely no acceptable reason. The words just bubbled out, as if the sac that held my thoughts had popped a leak. She looked to be in her late twenties—a small tattoo of a flower inside her right wrist, a single earring—and was pleasant and attentive, obviously well trained in the art of hospitality. I could see her trying to think of something to say in return. Her lips twitched. A small flex was visible in the muscles of her cheeks. But she was stuck, frozen. Nowhere in hotel school had the instructors offered advice on what to do when a robed man checked in, said something about not eating, and was accompanied by a hatchet-thrower who looked like he needed an hour with the nearest therapist.

We rode the glass elevator up to our room. While Rinp was using the toilet, I switched on the television just long enough to hear a brief report about Russians stuck in a convoy on route to

Kyiv, then I snapped the screen dark again and lay on the bed, face-up. The world oppressed me for those moments. Again. I admit it. The house was sold. I felt adrift, hungry, foolish, a failure at too many things. I took a breath, listened to Rinpoche humming while he washed his hands, and realized that it was all just thought, a sour stream running from the loss of Jeannie, the sale of our home, the absence of my children, the end of my career, the brutality of Putin's war, the divisiveness of American politics, all the way to my embarrassment at Stumpy's—not the failure to master the art of hatchet-throwing, but the failure to realize how little it meant, in the scope of things.

I took a breath, another breath. Just thoughts, I told myself. Another breath. "Ready for the meditation now, Otto?" Rinpoche asked. And I was.

That night I dreamt I was eating a bowl of tomato soup, so thick it was almost a stew. A fly had fallen into the middle of the bowl and I'd been too slow to scoop it out, and now it had sunk into the soup, and in the dream I realized I'd either have to stop eating entirely and waste the meal, examine each spoonful looking for the tomato-soup-soaked dead fly, or eat the soup, fly and all, and not worry about it. The dream ended before I made a decision.

Eighteen

I woke to a lengthy email from my wonderful sister. She was writing to inform me that she was in Iowa, where my heretofore perfectly dependable 2016 Toyota Camry had started "making terrible noises" the previous afternoon, as she pulled into a restaurant lot for lunch, had broken down completely before she even reached a parking place, and was now "in the shop." "It's fine, though, Otto," she wrote. "I trust the nice mechanic at the garage where the car got towed, and I'm enjoying myself getting to know Cedar Rapids."

I had to work hard to set aside the visions this email elicited: the 'nice mechanic' calling my sister to say how sorry he was, but the Camry needed a new engine and, with the supply-chain problems and everything, the rising costs, Covid, staff shortages, the war and other troubles, she'd either have to write him a check for $9,500 before he even started the repairs, or she'd have to sell him the car for half that amount. But all I wrote back to my sister was, "Okay, Seese. Glad you're all right, and I hope they take care of whatever the problem might be."

Once she received the email, she called, spoke to me for two minutes, and sounded happy. Relieved at my calm response, maybe, or at being in Cedar Rapids—she liked new places. Or simply because she was who she was, a kind woman in a happy marriage that had produced a wonderful daughter. Before hanging up, she asked me to remind Rinpoche that we had a breakfast meeting scheduled that morning at a place called Tatte Bakery and Cafe, just down the street from the hotel. She asked me to tell him how much she loved him, and that she'd call again later in the day, on his phone.

We hung up with "I love yous." I passed on both the reminder and the love to Rinpoche. He nodded, smiled at Seese's message, and said only one word: "Richard!"

I left a very large tip for the woman who would clean the room, nestling the bills safely under a glass on the bathroom sink, and we packed up, deposited our bags in the truck we'd parked in the underground garage, and headed out for our meeting.

It was sunny, windy, and cold, typical March weather in that part of the world. Rinpoche was wearing his robe and his pistachio-colored, yarmulke-like, wool hat. "Seese set up a meeting, I guess," I said, trying not to say what I had succeeded in not saying to my sister: *would it be too much to ask that I knew the schedule a day ahead of time?!* Another lesson. Why did I need to know the schedule a day ahead of time? So I could think about it, imagine it, prepare for it?

We walked a block and a half along Wisconsin Avenue—a wide street, noisy with trucks and busses, the sidewalk busy with women and men heading off to work—and soon stepped into a bright, spacious coffeeshop. Having eschewed the previous evening's meal, I felt my eyes travel immediately to a glass case filled with a sumptuous array of pastries. My mood lifted. Chocolate croissants, almond croissants, cakes, scones, muffins, Danishes. They weren't technically desserts, so there would be no breaking of the Lenten fast I'd managed to break several times already by then. I could smell strong coffee being brewed, and hear the delightful *pssssh* of a cappuccino machine, and the tall young man who greeted us seemed to me to be bursting with pride at the delicacies offered. And rightly so. Rinp and I made our selection—tea for him, iced coffee for me, a pastry each and one to share—and carried the plates and mugs over to a window table on the far side of the coffee bar. An elderly man was sitting there. He was wearing thick spectacles and a fine gray suit, white button-down shirt, light blue tie, and on his head was an actual yarmulke. When we approached, he stood and shook our hands, introduced himself in a very quiet voice as "Richard," and sat back down again as if the greeting had exhausted him.

How Rinpoche and Richard knew each other, I had no idea. But that was more or less standard procedure for these meetings. Everywhere we'd ever traveled, from Las Vegas to Rome, from Westchester County, New York, to Winthrop, Massachusetts, my brother-in-law had these 'friends', who seemed on almost intimate terms with him, as if they'd known him for many lifetimes, as if they'd traveled with him from Skovorodino in southern Siberia to Rinpoche's meditation centers in Italy and Croatia, and then to the farm in North Dakota; as if, over the past decades, they'd kept up with him via monthly emails, greeting cards, or phone conversations; as if they'd co-written or edited his seven books on care of the interior world. Rinpoche was famous; I sometimes forgot that. To me, he was best friend, spiritual advisor, my sister's husband, my kids' uncle, but to hundreds of thousands of people around the world, he was Volya Rinpoche, meditation master, spiritual teacher, guru, the latest sacred incarnation in a lineage of famous spirits. What I found interesting was both how varied these friends of his were, and how much I ended up liking almost all of them. Different as I might be from someone like Tom the former Celtics star, and Jarvis, the Washington-state friend who'd once given Rinpoche an antique pickup truck named Uma that happened to contain a stash of marijuana in the glovebox, we all shared, at a deep level, a kind of agreement with the things Rinpoche said and wrote about. That commonality transcended the more superficial differences.

As had been the case with Tom at Rossetti's Cafe, Rinpoche spent a little while catching up with Richard, and I enjoyed the food and drink and listened in. From the conversation, I gathered that Richard had lost his wife not long ago, and that he'd recently celebrated his 94th birthday. I could hear, as he spoke of his children, that, like me, he was a devoted father, that whatever his professional accomplishments, his feelings for his two sons and two daughters remained more important. And I could sense, too, that the veil of grief had not yet lifted.

He had an unusual way of speaking, almost as if he were writing the words with his mouth and tongue. He spoke so quietly that I had to lean forward to hear, and he pronounced each word separately, not running them together in a sentence, but 'typing' them out through his teeth so precisely and clearly that he could have given diction lessons.

After a few minutes, the conversation turned to the war in Ukraine, and I spoke up and said something about the horror of it all, about how I'd hoped we'd evolved beyond such things, in Europe at least, how I thought we'd learned our painful lessons.

At that comment, Richard shifted his eyes to me—watery, wrinkled, intelligent, old-man's eyes—and said, "I was born in Vienna in 1921."

Just that. *I was born in Vienna in 1921.* That, and the yarmulke.

I was cast abruptly into what Natasha might have called another 'head-space.' I suddenly felt that the horror that had been haunting me on TV, radio, in the newspaper headlines, and on my computer screen, had taken a seat at the table. Richard was still looking at me. I wanted to ask, and didn't want to ask. Something appeared at the corners of his lips, the shadow of a smile perhaps, not self-pity but an expression that might be called 'wry', as if he'd seen too much of what the world could offer and was weary of it, resigned to it; as if he'd been intimate with the worst of it, and human life no longer had any chance of surprising or disappointing him.

"When I was seventeen," he said, "my parents managed to get me out of Vienna. On a train. I will always remember waving good-bye to them at the station, my mother weeping, my father trying not to weep. I came through London to New York, and lived with an uncle and aunt in Brooklyn. They fed me and let me sleep on their sofa . . . for six years. I finished high school, attended and graduated from City College, and for the first part of that time I was sending letters back and forth to my parents. They, too, managed to escape Vienna. They fled to Poland, which, for a short while at least, seemed safe. Then, when Poland was divided east and west, they became separated, and I was writing to each of them every week, trying desperately to find a way to get them to America. However, in those days, the American State Department had set strict limits on the acceptance of Jews. Eventually I stopped hearing from my parents. I discovered later that my father had died in Majdanek, and my mother in the ghetto uprising in Warsaw."

"I'm sorry," I said.

"Yes, thank you. It was long ago." He touched his thick eyeglasses. "I had weak eyesight even then and, once I completed college, I was classified 4F. However, I insisted on changing that classification to 1A, and the Army agreed because, of course, I spoke fluent German and could be useful. I ended up—have you heard of the Ritchie Boys?"

"I have, yes."

"We ended up interrogating German prisoners of war. It was very interesting work. Some of them were reluctant to speak, and refused multiple times to answer the questions I put to them. In those cases, I'd call over my supervisor and I'd say, "This is one for the Russians," and immediately the German prisoner would tell us everything we asked. Immediately. Instantly. They knew the Russians. Even then."

"I'm sorry again," I said.

"No need, no need. I came home from my service and attended Yale Law School and I made a career of representing various oppressed groups. I did a great deal of work with the Native American population, especially at Pine Ridge. Have you heard of Pine Ridge?"

I nodded. "Rinpoche and I went through it on one of our road trips."

"A tragedy, is it not? A disgrace in a nation like ours."

"It is, yes, both."

"And then I worked in the government, for a time, concentrating on the scourge of human trafficking."

"You've seen the worst," I said.

"Some of the worst. Yes. Much of it. But do you know what is strange, Otto? I remember once, as a boy, standing in line, applying for a visa. In Vienna. The Nazis had come to the city by then—this was shortly after the *Anschluss*—and had been welcomed warmly by many Austrians, including some of our neighbors. I saw the Nazis force old Jewish men to scrub the streets after Kristallnacht, which was a terrible thing to witness. But, strangely, what I remember most vividly is standing in that line and having one of the Nazis, an officer, knock into me very rudely. He was walking past, and rather than walk around me, he shoved me aside. I nearly fell over. He didn't apologize, of course, and, of course, it should go without saying, they did much worse things than push a young boy. But I remember that moment with a peculiar vividness. It is etched into my memory. It was a kind of transgression of the unspoken laws of politeness, of decency. So minor compared to everything else, and yet, it seems somehow, even now, to stand as a kind of symbol for the rest of what they did, in Austria and elsewhere. That small moment. That willingness to cross a certain line that marks the human dignity of another person. I trace all of it to that moment. Do you think that's foolish of me?"

Richard's quiet, elegant speech had a hypnotic quality to it, and I felt as though I'd been immersed in his world, the awful world of Vienna, 1938. His question took me by surprise, and I needed a few seconds to realize he was actually asking it of me. "N-no, not at all," I heard myself say. "I haven't had anything remotely like that happen to me. Someone cutting me off in traffic. Being yelled at a couple of times on the subway. My parents were killed by a drunk driver some years ago. Other than that, I've had a very comfortable, very safe life without any trauma."

"Yes, but Rinpoche told me you lost your wife," he said.

"I did. But she wasn't killed by another person, she—"

"Yes, but nevertheless you were touched deeply by, what should we call it?"

"What we don't want to happen," I said, without thinking.

Richard stretched his lips again into the sad smile. "Ah, yes. *What we don't want to happen.* That is the perfect way to express it. *What we don't want to happen.*" He reached across the table then and put one of his hands over one of Rinpoche's, but he kept his eyes on me. "One of my grandchildren is passionate about Legos, do you know what they are?"

"Sure."

"He is eleven. He constructs these beautifully elaborate cities and castles. He is really good at it. I watch him and sometimes even manage to get down on the floor and work with him, which he enjoys. And sometimes as I'm doing that, I think of the beautifully elaborate lives so many of us—people like you and me—construct in this country now, gardens of every kind of pleasure. To the extent possible, at least for a time, many of us are able to wall off those gardens from the pains and difficulties, the terrors and horrors. Of course, I never want my grandson to experience such things. I pray that he never experiences them."

"But *you* did."

"I did, yes. But my point is that perhaps everyone does, to some degree or another, at some time or another." His hand still covered Rinpoche's. "This man," he squeezed Rinpoche's hand and released it, "taught me, among other things, to see the potential for that pain in every person. It has strengthened my own faith greatly. It sounds maudlin perhaps, Otto, but really it is not. I see that potential. Whenever I meet or speak with another person, I try to see it, and it breeds in me what might be called 'a vibrant compassion', and I have tried to use that vibrancy to alleviate what pain I could. The alternative, it seems to me, is self-pity."

"But there's so much of it we can't alleviate."

"Exactly. I could not save my own parents, and I will carry the guilt of that until my final breath. They saved me. I could not save them in return. We do what we can. We take some enjoyment for ourselves—I, for example, come here every day for their delicious chocolate muffins. I love to spend time with my grandchildren. I love to watch soccer on the television. I love to read the great novels and listen to opera. I have tried, I still try, to do what I can to ease the suffering on this earth, and I'm sure you do the same. The rest of it we have to allow to be, as painful as that is for us. We have to care for ourselves and our loved ones. We have to serve others to the extent we are able. And the rest of it we have to allow to be. It is awful, is it not, the human predicament? Awful and beautiful."

At that point, Rinpoche stood up and left the table. He returned after a moment with one of those long, twisted sticks of dough, lightly coated in sugar. He broke it into four pieces and handed a piece to Richard and one to me, kept one, and left the fourth piece on the plate. He put the sweet twisted stick into his mouth and bit off half of it and he looked at me as he chewed. I would describe the expression on his face as *mischievous*. He was up to something, I knew him well enough to see that. But he didn't speak. Richard was smiling at him, almost laughing. Rinpoche kept chewing, watching me, until I said, "What?"

He pointed the uneaten part of the stick at me and said, "You a human being," as if he'd just discovered that fact, or as if I had. And then he left me hanging there, wondering what he meant by leaving one piece of the pastry on the plate and dividing the rest among us. Richard was nodding like a master Zen student who'd solved a difficult koan.

"You lost me just a little bit, Rinp," I said.

"On the plate is the part of life we cannot change," Richard suggested quietly. He looked at me through his thick lenses. "You put it so beautifully, Otto: *what we do not want to happen.* For human beings, there is and always will be that element to our lives. What we do not want to happen."

Rinpoche dipped the sugary stick into his tea and said, "I like this dessert wery much. How you call it?"

Nineteen

After bidding Richard a fond good-bye in front of Tatte, Rinpoche and I walked back to the hotel and took the elevator down to the parking garage. "I want to try in-the-city driving again now, Otto," he said.

"I thought you were sick of driving."

"Not sick now of it anymore. I rested from it."

"Okay, Rinp, but it's pretty tricky getting a pickup out of one of these garages. The spaces are tight."

"I want to try."

"Okay."

Rinpoche took his place in the driver's seat. He put both hands on the wheel and squeezed. I watched him take several deep breaths and bring his concentration to bear. After a minute or so of preparations, he put the truck in drive and moved it forward a couple of feet, then stopped. "How it's lookin' on that side?" he asked.

"Fine. Take it slow."

"Taking it," he said. He moved the truck forward another two feet, turning it a few degrees left, then stopped and looked out his window at the Mercedes SUV parked there, so close now he could have reached out and wiped the dead white moth from the front corner of the hood. Three feet to my right stood a square concrete post. We had a little room there. Opposite us was another line of cars, most of them backed into place so it felt like their headlights were a row of eyes, watching Rinpoche's performance.

"You good on that side?"

"Little bit close, Otto."

"Okay, just straighten out the wheel and go forward almost as far as you can, then stop, turn the wheel to the right, and back up. You should have enough room then."

At that moment, someone in a new blue Audi drove around the corner to our right, and I could tell by the way the car came to a halt and by the look on the driver's face that he was in a hurry. Maybe the hotel breakfast hadn't appealed, and he was eager to find a local diner before heading off to a sales meeting in the District; or he'd had an argument with the person with whom he'd spent the night and was anxious to flee the scene; or that same person was up at street level with her luggage and was known to spark a temper when kept waiting. Rinpoche didn't see this other driver at first, and didn't seem to read the signals I was reading. He moved us forward another two feet, safely avoiding the Mercedes and the square post, but stopping well short of the line of cars opposite. I tried not to look at the driver in the blue Audi. Rinpoche was stuck there, befuddled. "Now what, Otto?" he said.

"Now go forward another few feet and then stop, turn the wheel hard to the right, put the truck in reverse, and you should be able to back up far enough to get out."

"Okay."

We went forward one foot, and stopped. The driver to our right hit the horn. Once. Somewhere between a tap and a blast. I waved at him, an apology.

"A little farther forward, Rinp."

Another foot. Stop.

"Now swing the wheel all the way to the right, put the shift in reverse, and back up slowly."

The Audi driver leaned on the horn.

"He's mad on me," Rinpoche said.

"Don't worry about him." I put a hand up to the window, a gesture that said *We see you. We're having trouble here. We're trying.* And I noticed that the driver—a thirtyish man in white shirt and tie—made an unfriendly gesture in return. With both hands.

Rinpoche very carefully turned the wheel all the way to the right, shifted the truck into reverse and backed up one foot.

"Good?" he said, turning to look at me. I saw his eyes move sideways to the angry driver. Rinpoche waved and smiled. The man was spitting out words we couldn't quite hear.

"Great, now back up a bit more."

If you didn't know Rinpoche, if you'd been the man in the dress shirt and tie, driving the new blue Audi, you would have thought the driver of the pickup was going slow on purpose just to be annoying—especially after the friendly wave. Rinpoche wasn't being annoying on purpose, of course, but the other driver couldn't know that. More blaring of the horn. The man was pounding on the steering wheel now. Rinpoche was in reverse but moving the truck very, very slowly, inch by inch. "It's working," he said.

"Okay now, stop before you hit the pole."

"Stopping."

"Now put the shift in drive, turn the wheel the other way, go forward, and you should be all set."

The man was leaning on the horn now, a steady blast. I rolled down my window, and he stopped and rolled down his window. "New driver, sorry," I called.

And he called back, using a familiar expression that still

can't be used on TV. I noticed that he wasn't very tall and that he had a wide, oval face.

"The bad word," Rinpoche said, and now we were free of the space and moving, at about four miles an hour, up the narrow ramp that led to the place where the black and white arm either raised up to signal that you could pass, or failed to do so. The Angry Man was three inches behind us.

"You got the ticket, right, Rinp?"

"Think so," he said.

He pulled very slowly up to the machine, put the truck in park, and spent ten or fifteen seconds fishing through the pockets of his robe before producing a mangled ticket.

BLAM, BLAM BLAM! Went the horn behind us. I was certain the wrinkles and folds of the ticket would keep it from registering in the machine, and fairly sure the little man with the wide face would jump out of his Audi, pistol in hand, and, driven over the edge of sanity by having had to wait a few minutes longer than he should have, would come up to the door of the truck and commit murder, with Rinpoche and me as the victims. Similar things had been known to happen. Moreso of late.

But, somehow, on the third try, Rinpoche managed to insert the ticket. A circular light went on. The arm lifted. Rinpoche waved to the man behind us, in a friendly way. BLAM! BLAM! More of the bad word, and we were out in the Bethesda sunshine, turning onto Wisconsin Avenue. Safe. The blue Audi cut into the other lane and roared past us as far as the next stoplight.

"Thanks, Otto. Sorry," Rinpoche said. "And sorry to the man."

"He'll live."

"Maybe he had to be going to the hospital to seeing his wife!"

"Maybe."

"Wery in a hurry!"

"We all are. All the time." I was hoping we wouldn't reach the light while it was still red and have to stop beside the Audi. The evening news was speckled with road-rage stories. Every month or so there would be a report of someone in California who'd shot and killed a passenger in another car because he'd been cut off. Or someone in Ohio who'd jumped out at a red light, furious at another driver, and smashed the windshield with a baseball bat. Or someone in Kentucky who ran another driver off the road for a minor offense, perceived or real. We'd gotten more or less used to it, the way we'd gotten more or less used to schoolkids growing up with the sound of gunfire, the way we'd gotten more or less used to candidates spending small fortunes to get elected, to footwear made in China, and wildfires destroying millions of acres in California. I understood why the man was angry. I probably would have been angry, too, if I'd been late for a meeting and encountered a driver in a pickup taking four minutes to get out of a parking garage. A four-minute delay had come to be a reason for fury, maybe even violence. We'd gotten used to that, too. For a moment I thought about the new life my sister and Rinpoche had planned for me. I was going to live on the farm where I'd been raised, help out with the meditation retreats they ran there, do a little gardening, take long walks, maybe find a doubles partner in Dickinson and work on my tennis game, maybe take up cooking, watercolor painting, or train for a five-K road race that permitted stretches of walking. I was going to step off the conveyor belt of city life, downshift, leave the superhighway for the quieter two-lane roads of less-than-idyllic North Dakota. At that moment, with the traffic light going green in front of a mass of growling machinery, I felt ready for the change.

Continuing with the theme of The Giving Project, we headed over to the headquarters of the Cystic Fibrosis Foundation and, while Rinpoche waited in the truck, I went upstairs to the offices and handed over a large check. "Friends of ours had a child with CF," was all I said, though there was so much more I could have told her about those friends, their son who'd died at nineteen, and the miserable disease that had taken him. The young woman asked if she could put me on the mailing list, and I said sure, why not, told her I'd be moving soon and gave her my email address, then rode the elevator back down to street level. We followed a winding residential road through northwestern D.C., at one point hearing, through the tops of the open windows, what sounded like the chants of demonstrators. "What is?" Rinpoche asked.

"I don't know. There are a lot of embassies in this neighborhood. Maybe that noise is people in front of the Russian embassy, protesting."

Miraculously, we managed to come upon a parking space near the National Gallery. The space was at the end of a line of cars, and did not require parallel parking skills, a circumstance for which I was grateful. When Rinpoche turned off the truck, he looked at me and the big smile bloomed. "In-the-city-driving," he said proudly, and I patted him on the knee and told him he'd done a great job.

It had been many years since Jeannie and I had taken the kids to see the exhibits at the National Gallery, and I'd forgotten how grand the building itself was, with its wide concrete stairway and huge entrance doors. In those days there hadn't been a need for metal detectors at the entrance—which, it seems to me, says a great deal about the devolution of human society over the past two decades. Once Rinpoche and I passed through the doors and the metal detectors, the place felt to me like a refuge from that downward slide, from the anger and rush of the streets. Almost a sacred place.

We climbed a marble stairway to the second floor and took our time there, wandering from room to room, past the Monets and Sargents and Bierstadts and Cropseys. There was a wonderful display by the Harlem photographer James Van Der Zee, who, in the first half of the twentieth century had made portraits of middle-class African Americans, often to commemorate their weddings or other special occasions. At times he'd taken the liberty of hand-drawing a piece of jewelry onto the portrait of a young bride, giving her a gold bracelet or brooch she never could have afforded. I loved the expressions on the faces there, the dignity and joy and pride, and, as we moved on, I loved the massive paintings of western scenes, the near-perfect representations of the grand mountains, lakes, and forests. Thomas Cole's incredible series, The Voyage of Life, sent me into a momentary reverie of my own: Childhood, Youth, Manhood, and—soon enough—Old Age.

Rinpoche seemed entranced. He moved from painting to painting at about the same pace as he'd moved out of the parking garage, in no hurry at all. The word that came to my mind was *communing,* as if he were making some kind of soul-to-soul connection with the artists, or with the canvases themselves. Most of the paintings done by women—Vigee' Le Brun, Leyster, Moriset, Cassatt, Bonheur, Ruysch—were of domestic scenes, well-off mothers and daughters posing in a living room, say, because that was the life of those artists then, circumscribed by the rules of their time. Quiet, interior, safe, lacking adventure but full of human connection.

There was a Cezanne—Hamlet at Payennet near Gardanne—on loan from the White House, with a notice beneath it saying that taking photos of this particular painting was prohibited. I didn't understand why. It happened to be the painting Rinpoche seemed most taken with, a gorgeously simple depiction of a cluster of boxy houses with ochre walls and red roofs set against blue mountains in the distance. He sat across from it for so long that I made a tour of the nearby rooms of elegant furniture, came back, and he hadn't moved. I sat beside him. He turned to me with the big smile and, gesturing toward the painting with one hand, said, "The opposite of war, Otto." And then swung his arm around to encompass the entire collection. "This place the opposite of war."

We finished with a tour of the sculpture gallery, and all the while I was pondering the lives of the people who'd created the works on display. They'd devoted decades to honing a craft, spent countless hours in a parlor, or field, in a studio constructing a desk of inlaid mahogany, putting oil on canvas in a certain way, shaping clay, cutting marble. There was no practical reason for it. Those talented souls weren't curing diseases, inventing a new kind of stove, or building a company that would employ thousands. What they *were* doing, it seemed to me, was saying: *This, look at this!* Urging us to pay attention to color and texture, to the miracle of a human face caught in a moment of joy or pain, to the gray slope of a mountain reflected in a still pond, or to the intricacies of a surface of inlaid wood or textured marble. Cezanne had understood that there was nothing at all plain and ordinary about a hillside covered with plain and ordinary houses. Monet and Matisse and Sargent and Cassatt had understood that there was nothing plain and ordinary about a flower garden, an angry sea, a woman and her sister conversing on a sofa, a mother drying her daughter's skin after a bath. *Look at this!* They were saying. Rinpoche was correct. It was pure appreciation for life. The opposite of war.

Twenty

I was behind the wheel as we took I-95 south out of the Capital toward Fredericksburg. We were silent with each other for a time, no conversation, no radio. The feeling of peace—the National Gallery's great gift—clung to us like cool evening air after a hot day, and no amount of frenzied highway driving seemed able to disturb it.

A former colleague had recommended an Italian restaurant in Fredericksburg—Orofino, it was called—and said they served good pizza and excellent, inventive salads. But it was too early to eat again, and so, instead of paying a visit to that city, we turned off on Route 3 toward Culpeper, heading for that evening's destination—conveyed again, last-minute, via a text from my sister—Lynchburg, Virginia. "You'll stay in Lynchburg for one night, Otto," she'd emailed me. There was no further explanation except, "I've made a reservation at a nice place there, the Lynchburg Grand Hotel. It looks okay."

Did I argue? No.

Did I make alternate suggestions, telling my sister about the salads at Orofino, or that it might be more fun or convenient to be spontaneous, maybe see a great old-fashioned inn along our route and just decide to stay there, spur of the moment? No.

Did I ask why Lynchburg and not Roanoke or Blacksburg or Danville? Absolutely not.

I might be a slow learner, but I'm a learner. I'd had five decades of experience with Seese's sudden pronouncements and offbeat habits. And I'd had three other long road trips with Rinpoche, trips on which Seese had usually made some or all of the arrangements. I knew enough by then to realize that a) there must be some reason why she'd chosen Lynchburg, rather than Roanoke, Blacksburg, or Danville, and b) I would discover that reason, as my parents used to say, 'in good time.'

So I bypassed Fredericksburg, let go of staying there long enough to test the pizza at Orofino, and took Route 3, west.

For a short stretch then it was chain-heaven. Or chain-hell, depending on your point of view. We passed every imaginable national chain—food places, fast and otherwise; pharmacies; building supplies. There was even a chain sex shop, Adam and Eve, which I'd noticed on other drives in other parts of the country. But there was some creativity, too, in the signs for non-chain establishments: Unmentionables Lingerie, Valhalla Martial Arts, The Plumbing Police, The Church of the Messiah. Soon, spurred by the first twinges of hunger, I noticed a restaurant advertising "World's Greatest Catfish" and then a truck with "Follow me to Your Next Great Meal" painted on the back. But it was still too early to stop.

We passed into Spotsylvania County and saw a patch of tract homes, which elicited in me the same feeling elicited by the chains, and made me think of Shelsa again, giving speeches about spirituality and capitalism and receiving death threats. I sometimes worried that I looked too deeply into things. There was nothing wrong with having dinner at Olive Garden, or a fast lunch at Burger King, or with buying some two-by-fours at Lowe's. Nothing wrong with living on a cul de sac in a large home that looked exactly like all the other large homes on your street. I don't judge people for such things, really I don't. And

143

yet, there seemed to me something out of balance about it all. The fact was that Home Depot and Lowe's had put out of business several family-owned lumberyards where I'd purchased materials in my years of making small repairs around the house. The fact was that the Olive Gardens sucked the life out of small Italian restaurants owned by people who'd invested all their savings then slaved away for decades but couldn't possibly match the prices, or the available parking, or the predictability for travelers who didn't know the area. It was the loss of that *life* that troubled me, the quirkiness of the Mom and Pops, the uniqueness of individually-designed homes built by a small crew of craftsmen for whom the job meant a year's pay.

I'd become an old crank, I suppose, but one of the things I'd always loved about my road trips with Rinpoche was what might be called 'the anti-chains,' and that intricacy and heterogeneity was being drained out of the national landscape now because someone had figured out it was more profitable to buy or build things in bulk. Profitable for whom, I wondered? For holding companies and big investors and hedge funds and corporations so large they took in more money in a week than some small nations did in a year? I wondered if I could broach the subject with my hedge-fund-executive son, but just then we came upon a sign for the Chancellorsville Battle Memorial, and my thoughts shifted.

On the other long trips with Rinpoche, I'd always made an effort to show him what I thought of as 'Americana'. By 2022, he'd been living in the U.S. for some fifteen years, so it might seem he should have become familiar with the country on his own. To some degree, that had, in fact, happened. Really, however, when he wasn't on the road with me, he was most often holed up at the retreat center he and my sister ran on what had once been our parents' farm. Beautiful place though that was, and wondrously peaceful as the meditation retreats made one feel, our farm was hardly a location from which one could glean wide personal experience of America—especially if one did not watch a lot of TV. Rinp's neighbor, Les Ingler, was hardly the kind of person who could expose him to the thousands of aspects of this country that reflected its deep and varied culture.

So, as we drove south, I'd been on the lookout for ways I might enhance my brother-in-law's understanding of our great land. Hence the hatchet-throwing and the National Gallery. Just west of Fredericksburg, we passed a sign saying that the Chancellorsville Battlefield was a mile ahead. The Civil War was a part of American history I suspected Rinpoche didn't know much about, and, in truth, I was no expert either, so when we came abreast of the entrance to the national park, I turned in.

The place was empty. Maybe three spots were taken in a parking area built for two hundred cars—it wasn't exactly tourist season—and when we stepped into the small visitors center there, the man behind the glass desk seemed overjoyed to have some company.

Beyond the desk, you turned left and made a brief tour through a maze of dioramas and other exhibits. There were scraps of Confederate and Union uniforms. There were written descriptions of the battles, along with paintings and old photos.

It turned out that at the Battle of Chancellorsville, General Lee, with a vastly outnumbered army of Rebels, had made a move of strategic genius that had forced General Hooker to order the retreat of his Union fighters. It had been a great victory for the South. In the course of it, however, Lee's best general, Thomas 'Stonewall' Jackson, had been accidentally wound-

145

ed by his own troops as he finished an evening reconnaissance on horseback. Shot in the arm, Jackson soon had to suffer that limb's amputation (the surgeon's tools were part of the display, and so primitive-looking that the idea of them being used to sever an arm gave me the chills). The operation went well enough, but Jackson contracted pneumonia soon after and died eight days later, his death being a major factor in the South's ultimate defeat.

Among the quotes shown on the displays was one by David Holt, a soldier in the 16th Mississippi regiment: "We halted in a pasture and broke ranks. Then came the reaction. All moved by the same impulse, we sat down on the wet ground and wept. Not silently, but vociferously and long."

Surgeon Henry Van Aaernam, of the 154th New York, was quoted as saying, "I never had a vivid description of hell, until I saw that battle . . . which I pray I may never experience again."

I was astounded to learn that, at Chancellorsville, an average of one man was killed or wounded every second—for five hours.

There were quotes from women whose homes and food stores had been raided by Union soldiers. There were several boards describing the contribution of freed slaves, members of the United States Colored Troops or USCT. The horror of it all—the battle fatigue, the carnage, the blood and smoke and screaming—was graphically displayed and described. It was all particularly moving to me because, on the day we visited the Chancellorsville memorial, the Russian Army was bombarding a maternity hospital in Mariupol, and terrorizing the city of Irpin on what they hoped was their route to Kyiv.

Rinpoche seemed moved, as well. As he'd done in the National Gallery, he stepped past the exhibits at his own pace, lagging behind me. He stood for long moments in front of the pictures, staring at the faces as if there were actually living, suffering men a few feet in front of him. I finished the tour some fifteen minutes before he did, thanked the man behind the desk, then went out and stood near the spot, only a few yards from the door, where Stonewall Jackson had been shot. It seemed to me half-real that such a battle could have taken place amid those quiet woods. And yet I knew it was real, just as I knew that what was happening in Mariupol and Irpin was real. Seeing the horrific scenes of the battle, one would have thought no human being would ever start a war again, and yet it kept happening, across the globe, throughout history. The reasons varied, but the results were always the same: death, suffering, bereavement, misery. Humanity seemed, on that day, not merely a slow learner, but a non-learner.

Rinpoche stepped out of the building at last, saw me, and came walking over. He said nothing—both the beauty of the National Gallery's paintings and the horror of the Civil War seemed to have rendered words useless—but on his wide brown face I felt I could read the suffering of the world, centuries of it, millennia of it. His expression reminded me of the sculpture of a bodhisattva I'd seen in another museum, in Boston. All the suffering was shown there, in marble, and yet, behind or beyond it there was something else, a reflection of eternal peace, it seemed to me. The shine of hope.

We walked back to the truck—yours truly sat behind the wheel again—and took the Route 20 shortcut to Route 29, passing signs that said it was the Constitution Highway, and other signs, too: *Sales and Repair for Pedal Steel Guitar. Need Prayer? Let us Pray for You.*

By then we were hungry enough to stop in the small town of Orange, Virginia, which seemed, at first, to offer nothing in the way of opportunities for nourishment. But after a brief stroll, I spotted a blackboard with FORKED chalked on it, and we discovered that a restaurant called Forked on Main was open, and we went in. "Looks fancy," Rinpoche said, running his fingers across a white tablecloth. The Grateful Dead were playing. We were greeted by a large, friendly fellow, who seated us at one of the clothed tables, and we both ordered the crab bisque—which came in a bowl shaped like a white pig—and a tasty beet salad with goat cheese and walnuts. Some kind of golf tournament was being shown on a small TV at the top of a nearby wall, and Rinpoche kept glancing at it. When the large man—owner and waiter and perhaps chef—checked in on us, he asked Rinpoche if he was a golfer. "Yes, wery much," Rinp answered.

"Cool. I like to bet on golf. You can get some pretty good odds."

At the word 'bet', Rinpoche perked up. In our travels out west we'd stopped occasionally at the small Native American casinos that dotted that part of America. I'd made those stops innocently, another attempt to convey the full sense of my country to my Tibetan-Siberian brother-in-law. But it had been a mistake. Rinpoche, it turned out, liked gambling a bit too much. He was lucky, of course—that didn't surprise me—but so lucky that he'd begun to think of casinos as larger, more-interesting ATMs. You always won. Or at least, *he* always won. Or at least he won most of the time. As was the case with other things he did, I could never quite be sure if he was actually nurturing a small addiction, or offering a lesson, but more than once I'd had to spend several minutes convincing him to leave the machines and tables.

"Really?" he asked the man. "You can bet on the golf?"

"Sure. You can make some good money. I like to go to the poker rooms over in West Virginia, too. You can bet on your phone now, but I don't let myself get the apps. If I want to gamble, I make myself drive all the way across the border and back. Keeps me, you know, in check."

"Good, good," Rinpoche said, and then, when the man left us, he turned his eyes from the screen to me and said, "How far is it, Otto, to the West Virginia?"

"Far," I lied, "really far. And we're going the opposite way."

That seemed to do the trick. We finished the meal, paid and left, made another short stroll along Orange's quiet main street, past a bank and a flower shop, the whole town—a pleasant place—having that air of being partially emptied-out. Maybe it was simply the case that everyone was at work at that hour, or that all the young people were away at college. But we passed only one or two other pedestrians, one or two empty shops, and I thought again about the chains, and hedge funds, Shelsa, America.

We took Route 15 out of Orange and then turned onto Route 231, passing through Gordonsville, Waldrop, and Kesick. It was, at first, a soothing, low-key, country drive, even though the trees had only just started to bud, and the landscape was not at its most vibrant. Still, after the Chancellorsville visit, that drive was a salve for my overactive mind. There were wineries, rolling pastureland, orchards, white board fences, an equestrian ring with jumps set up. We cruised past a stretch of horse farms, estates really, with names like Tall Oaks, Cloverdale, Mooring Farm, Tally Ho, Springdale, Primavera. I could imagine how gorgeous the area must be in summer, a kind of American paradise, families dining on the patio after a day of jumping and currying and whatever else people did with horses. "Nice place," Rinpoche said. "I miss the horses, Otto."

Farther south, the land turned more forested, and the places we passed seemed poorer, with small houses set behind yards littered with old cars and pieces of metal and plastic.

In the cool of late afternoon, we pulled into Lynchburg and checked into the Lynchburg Grand, which did not seem aptly named. With its piano and soft chairs, the large lobby sang of finer days, but the huge fifth-floor room felt as though it had been built in the Seventies or Eighties and not touched since. Perfectly clean, two beds, towels, shower, the necessary amenities. Just old.

Rinp and I made a walking tour of the commercial part of the city, and it was more of the same. The simplest way to say it is that Lynchburg had seen better days. The city was hilly, set on a slope that ran down to the wide, shallow-looking James River, and the main commercial streets ran perpendicular to that slope, like terraces on an Italian vineyard. Some of the old buildings were, in fact, grand, with impressive stone facades and tall windows, some having been built in the Art-Deco style I liked. And there seemed to be an abundance of parking garages. But about half the storefronts in that part of town were empty. A pawn shop, stores selling jewelry and musical instruments, or renting formal wear for proms and weddings, but mixed in among them were a multitude of glass storefronts with For Rent signs, a little graffiti scrawled on the foundation or windows. Here and there you could see the first shoots of new growth, a couple of bistros, some street art, but the larger sense was one of staleness, an old body all wrinkled, with missing teeth and stooped posture.

We passed a set of stairs climbing up past a monument to a confederate soldier, and a sign saying there was a time capsule buried there with Confederate money and the hair of Robert E. Lee's horse, Traveller. I mentioned that to Rinpoche and he said, "War and paintings today, Otto."

"Exactly."

"And horses."

Back in the room, I turned on the TV just long enough to see more of the reporting from Ukraine. By then, darkness had fallen, and we were hungry again, and I suggested we take a drive and try to find a place to eat.

Perhaps there are good eating places on the strip outside of Lynchburg. No doubt there are. We just didn't happen to find them on that night. I'd seen an ad for a poolroom that served food, and, still stinging from the ego bruise of Stumpy's Hatchet House, I drove us out to the address. I was known to play a fair game of pocket billiards and was hoping I might rehabilitate my reputation, at least in my own eyes, but the poolroom was hosting some kind of very loud music, the parking lot was packed, and we turned around and started back. I saw a Waffle House on the right. We pulled in. What can be more American than Waffle House? It seemed a good choice for a lesson in Americana. But part of the interior was roped off. We were pointed to a booth in the open section and then made to sit there for a very long time without being approached and asked for an order. I stared at the plastic encased menu, thinking, *no, no, not for me, fat and sugar and chemicals, no* and finally I stood up and Rinpoche followed, and we headed back to the truck.

"They don't like us in there," Rinpoche said.

"My northern accent, maybe."

"Or," he grabbed the skirt of his robe and pulled it out in front of him. "My clothes."

"They don't see that many Buddhist monks, I bet."

"I think maybe they were very tired, those people."

I'd given up by then. Painfully hungry and resigned to another night of not eating, I was heading back toward downtown Lynchburg when Rinpoche pointed to illuminated letters, L U, high on a hill in front of us. "I'm doing the talk there tomorrow, Otto," he said. "In the college."

"I don't think so, Rinp. That's Liberty University. It's famous, in a way. Very conservative, very Christian."

"Right. Yes. They asked me for a talk."

"You're joking."

He was shaking his head.

"Seese didn't say anything about it. Are you sure?"

"Sure, yes. Long time ago. Go up. Maybe they have food up there. We can check out the rumpus."

"The campus."

"Yes, to see."

Rinpoche was mistaken about the talk, I was sure of that. I knew there was zero chance that he'd been asked to speak at Liberty University, but, driven by hunger, I turned at the sign, and we climbed a steep hill and reached the quiet campus. A young couple was walking along one of the sidewalks. I pulled to the curb and asked if there might be a place to eat close by.

"No, but there are restaurants in town," the young man said.

They were a very clean and well-groomed couple, something out of 1950s America, and the polar opposite of the kinds of students I'd seen on the college campuses of my youth. I was about to make a U-turn and head back into town when I spotted what seemed to be a fried-chicken place just across a huge parking lot.

"Looks like food," Rinpoche said. "Why they didn't say to us?"

"No idea."

I parked, we stepped inside. The place was bright and lively, filled with young women and men of college age, not all of them as neat as the couple we'd seen on the nearby campus. You ordered at a small desk with a menu posted above. Fried chicken plates. Fried chicken sandwiches. Fried chicken bits. Fried chicken every way it's possible to have fried chicken. I no longer cared about the healthfulness of the food, because, at that moment, I could have climbed up onto the desk and eaten the menu. We ordered fried chicken sandwiches with sides of slaw, lemonade to drink, and I decided I'd change the tenor of the evening, the brutal energy of the afternoon, the vibe of this earth, by giving the friendly young woman who took our order a twenty-dollar bill as a pre-meal tip. It made her happy. And seeing her happy made me happy.

Rinpoche and I sat at a high-topped table and awaited the delivery of our dinner. Paging through a copy of the school newspaper someone had left there, I came upon an advertisement of sorts with a photo of Jerry Falwell, Sr., the founder of the Moral Majority, former president of Liberty University, and father of Jerry Falwell, Jr.—who was currently on an indefinite leave from the presidency because of an Instagram post he'd shared some months earlier. In that photo, taken on a yacht, he had his arm around a woman not his wife, their pants were unbuttoned, and he was holding what appeared to be an alcoholic drink in his free hand. I recalled reading another story about him, something of a sexual nature, that must have been even more troubling to the University's Board. In the advertisement, the senior Falwell was quoted from his book, *Strength for the Journey:* "People who do not believe in sin are already well on the way to being its victim. The first and greatest self-deceit is the fantasy that any one of us is invulnerable to deception by the Enemy."

I decided, as I often did, that this particular piece of Americana—the Jerry Falwell, Jr., story—would not be useful to Rinpoche's understanding of his adopted nation. And it would have taken too long to relate and explain, in any case. In the previous year, a couple of famous Buddhist teachers had been implicated in one kind of scandal or another—sexual exploits, unwanted advances, misuse of funds. And there were, of course, the thousands of scandals associated with Roman Catholic priests and Protestant clergy. No faith was immune. If Jerry Falwell, Jr., had indeed been deceived by "the Enemy," he certainly wasn't alone.

Women always seemed attracted to Rinpoche, sometimes intensely attracted, but I'd never sensed in him any kind of improper behavior. "*Creepy* is the last thing you'd call him," Natasha told me once when we were on the subject. And Natasha was an attractive young woman and the member of my immediate family who'd spent the most time with him. Sometimes— as when he carried the strip club card around New York City— he seemed improbably innocent, as if lust were a dimension of life alien to him. He didn't make sex jokes. He swam in a Speedo bathing suit that was arguably too small for him, but there was never the sense that he was self-consciously trying to show his body parts. One way I might explain it is to say that the ordinary 'sense-pleasures'—food, alcohol, sex—didn't appear to exert any particular magnetic attraction on Rinp's attention. He could enjoy a meal, or he could fast. He'd fathered a child, so, obviously, he and my sister were intimate with each other. But, in his solar system, those kinds of pleasures were more satellites than planets. The gravitational fields weren't very strong.

In a peculiar way, his innocence was matched by the woman who'd first taken our order, the one to whom I'd given the twenty-dollar tip. During a quiet moment at the front desk, she came over, stood near our table, and said, "Hi, I'm Andalusia. I just wanted to say hi to you both." She turned her very large, very green eyes to Rinpoche and said something that nearly knocked me off my chair: "You're the holy monk who's going to speak to us tomorrow, aren't you?"

"Yes."

"We're so excited to have you. We're Christians, but we like to study other religions, too, in order to strengthen our own faith by comparison. Which is why we invited you!"

"What do you do in your faith?" Rinpoche asked her.

"We place our full trust in Jesus," Andalusia said, in a way that might open her, in certain of the circles in which I traveled, to mockery. The lilting voice, the smile, the reverent pronunciation of the name of her Lord. Rinpoche, however, a stranger to mockery and cynicism, seemed able to meet her on some common ground.

"Jesus wery good, wery strong," he said.

"Yes!" Andalusia clapped her hands together. "You're exactly right. Strong, yes! We pray that His strength will flow into us!"

Rinpoche smiled, nodded, sipped his lemonade. "How you pray?" he asked.

"Oh, we have a daily offering. We pray for anyone who needs our prayers. We pray for the atheists and the agnostics. My own roommate—I live off campus, I'm a senior—is an agnostic, unfortunately. I've asked the Lord if I should try to help her, but He's told me He holds her in His love, and everything will turn out fine for her."

"Good, good," Rinpoche said, with great earnestness. "Me, too, the same," he said, "I pray for people."

Andalusia's lovely smile bloomed again. "I'm so happy to meet you and so excited to hear you speak. What are you going to talk about, do you know?"

"Never know till last last minute."

155

She clapped her hands again. "That's wonderful! You let the Lord put the words into your mouth when you need them!"

"Yes, wery much. Maybe tomorrow I get some good words. We see." And Rinpoche went into one of his extended fits of chuckling, nodding his head hopefully, amused at the possibility that the right words might not arrive. "Sometimes they come out not so good!"

Andalusia reached out and touched him tenderly on the shoulder. "Oh, I'm sure it will be fine. I'll pray tonight that you'll be granted the gift of true speech."

"Thank you," Rinpoche said. "And tell the cook we have his compliments for this food."

"Oh, I will. What nice people you are." She swung her eyes to me, made something resembling the start of a curtsey, and returned to her duties.

I chewed a bite of the deeply fried chicken and looked out one of the side windows at the dark parking lot and, beyond it, the Liberty campus. A chorus of something like mockery was singing quietly in my inner ear; I couldn't help it. But overwhelming that chorus, charging right past it, was a type of paternal fear. How would such a young woman fare in the real world? If she thought her roommate's agnosticism was 'unfortunate,' what would happen to her when she encountered the rough-and-tumble of the secular life, without a campus of like-minded students, teachers, and counselors to console and support her? Would she find a commune somewhere and live with fellow Evangelical Christians? Would her workplace be free of sex jokes, curse words, flirting, nastiness, and the cynicism of the educated elite? In a million years I couldn't imagine her surviving in, say, New York City, or at one of the colleges my own children had attended. She'd be a target for bullies of various kinds, for men who wanted to seduce her into sin, for ridicule.

She'd be offended by textbooks that drew a picture of a world that would seem to her a cauldron of the purest evil. I watched her at her raised desk, a kind of pulpit, watched her smiling at the customers in line, explaining the menu, taking their money, making change, as open-hearted and unguarded as a person could possibly be.

I turned back to Rinpoche, who was carefully forking the last of a really decent coleslaw from the small plastic cup in which it had been served. "A nice girl," I said.

"Nice, nice, yes, Otto."

"Innocent, kind of. I'd worry about her if I were her dad."

Rinpoche stopped trying to capture the last mayonnaised shreds of cabbage and looked at me. "In this world," he said.

"This harsh world."

A nod. "Maybe tomorrow they don't like what I speak to them."

"I was shocked, honestly, when you said they'd invited you. I thought you were joking, or mixing things up. This college is famous for, you know, a certain brand of Christianity that isn't particularly open-minded."

Another nod. Another stab at the coleslaw. The tiniest wrinkle of worry on the wide brown face.

"Maybe just let them ask you questions instead of giving one of your usual talks," I suggested.

His face brightened. He reached across the table and tapped me lightly on top of my shoulder with one finger. "Sometimes you very wise, my good Otto." he said.

And I know I will always remember him saying that.

Twenty-One

That night I had an evil dream. It could have come from the double-fried chicken, or the conversation with Andalusia. It could have been because I looked up some old online information on Jerry Falwell, Jr. Or it could have been my fear of what awaited us at Liberty University.

Who knows where dreams have their roots?

I dreamt that Rinpoche and I were the target of a mob. The mob was composed of clean-cut young men and women, all of them—even the women—wearing neckties, all of them pointing at Rinpoche and me, narrowing their eyes, cursing us loudly and in unison. I awoke in the dark room and stared at the ceiling for a time, listening to the sorrowful whine of a freight train in the distance. I'd grown up hearing that sound, and have always loved it, but that night it seemed to me a cry of No! Nooooo! For a short while I wondered if the universe might be set up the way Andalusia believed it was, with a select group of devout, conservative Christians destined for glory, and the rest of us headed for the fire. That thought had no legs, as we say. No staying power. It flickered onto the screen of my interior world like a spark from a campfire, then floated up and away into the darkness, leaving just one faint red scratch across my mind that has long since disappeared.

Next morning, Rinp and I rose early and walked down the breezy, chilly main drag as far as a place called Batter Bar Crepes, which boasted large pane windows facing the street, and old church pews for seating. Two pleasant young women

158

operated the counter and stove, and the avocado BLT crepes they served us, wrapped in a cone of brown paper and accompanied by robust coffee, were delicious.

As we ate, I watched Rinpoche carefully, looking for signs of nervousness. I should have known better. He was there, where he always resided, in the moment, eating attentively and appreciatively, chewing, nodding, taking a sip of coffee and looking up at me, raising his slim eyebrows in a way that echoed my positive feelings about the meal. I admit that, over the years of our acquaintance, I'd been waiting for the modern American world, a world of haste and fear and an encyclopedia of plans and worries, to make inroads upon my brother-in-law's quiet interior life. I was thinking, that morning, about how much to tip the cleaning woman when we returned to the hotel, how the creperie managed to survive if it was always this quiet at the breakfast hour, if the city of Lynchburg would rebound, and, mainly, what the reception would be like at Liberty University; I was anticipating seeing my son later that day, and wondering how to ease the small trouble that seemed to have sprouted between us since his college years; I was wondering if the twinge in my chest was a sign that the Afib might be returning.

Rinpoche was eating breakfast.

We walked back to the hotel, checked out, and made the twenty-minute drive through the town and uphill to what I had come to think of as The Clean Place. The students looked clean, the buildings gleamed, the dormant lawns were immaculate. Exactly on time, fifteen minutes before the presentation, we were met by a thin, blond young man in a blue down vest, white dress shirt, and tan khakis, and ushered into a modern auditorium with balconies and circular seating. The auditorium was already full: several hundred students, a line of faculty members in the front row. As we entered, a quiet murmur lifted itself up against the ceiling. What little I knew about Liberty University made me suspect that the school didn't entertain a lot of speakers in maroon robes and shaved heads.

But, at first, everyone was exceedingly polite. A front row seat had been saved for me, a comfortable chair set mid-stage for the guest of honor. A female student clipped the microphone onto the collar of Rinpoche's robe, then turned to the audience and, without benefit of enhanced sound said, "The Religious Studies and Community Club is pleased to welcome today's guest speaker, Mr. Volya Rinpoch. Mr. Rinpoch is the author of seven books on Buddhist spirituality and has spoken at venues around the globe. He currently resides in North Dakota"—a spurt of applause from the back of the room—"where, with his wife, Cecelia, he runs a meditation retreat. Please give a warm Liberty welcome to Mr. Volya Rinpoch."

Polite applause. When it ebbed to silence, Rinpoche took a couple of long breaths, as he typically did before speaking, looked down at his folded hands as if waiting for the Lord to give him the good words, then raised his eyes to the crowd. "Thank you," he said. "Maybe I don't speak in perfect grandma, but I'm hoping you can understand the words." Another slow breath. "I was thinkin' last night maybe after we had a nice conversation with one of the students here, I was thinkin' that could be better instead of me making talk, talk, talk, if you have questions and I try to answer them."

Silence. A restless stirring, a flutter of whispers. I felt the woman next to me, who had introduced herself as a Professor of Biblical Studies, shifting uncomfortably in her seat. She turned her face toward me—I could sense her in my peripheral vision—as if she wanted to make a comment. I kept my eyes straight ahead because the comment I imagined her making was *I thought we were paying him to* speak!

Rinpoche waited for a minute or so longer than most people would have waited. Then said, "I promise I give you long answers!" And a few people laughed.

We endured another awkward moment, and then, as if to prime the pump, the professor beside me raised her hand, stood up, and said, "I wonder, Sir, if you could say a few words about Jesus Christ, Our Lord."

Rinpoche fixed her with unblinking eyes. He waited to see if she was finished, then nodded a few times as if he'd been expecting exactly that question, and said, "Jesus was wery great Master!"

Uncomfortable laughter skittered across the audience. *Uncertain* laughter, I'd call it. I could sense that the attendees were withholding judgment, at least for the first few minutes; that they were confused, curious, perhaps suspicious, but impeccably polite. All of that might simply have been in my own thoughts, my preconceived notions, my read of the mood.

"Not God?" the woman persisted.

"Sure, God!" Rinpoche said. "Yes wery much God!"

"Then why don't you worship him and call yourself a Christian?"

"Christian, Buddhist, Jewish, Hindu, these are only the words."

"They are, yes, but—"

"And I think maybe the words not the important part. The important part how you live, how you treat unto others the way you want being treated. Jesus said so, yes?"

"Absolutely."

"So, for me, I'm not paying for the most attention to what label you call me. Jesus wasn't the Christian. Buddha wasn't the

Buddhist. They came to human form to us to show us a way to be in this life."

The professor sat down with a small, unsatisfied, "hmph", and suddenly there was a flurry of questions, the first by a young woman who sounded a lot like Andalusia. The same lilting intonation, the same upbeat voice. I turned to look: not her. "Sir," she began, "if I can follow up on Mrs. Smethen's good question, do you believe there can be more than one God?"

Rinpoche looked at her, not unkindly but attentively, as if trying to see into her depths, the place from which thoughts emerged and formed themselves into words, or action. Again, he took an extra few seconds to answer.

"Did you understand my question?" the young woman asked.

Rinpoche nodded. "I don't wery much say the word 'God'," he said.

"Why not? Don't you believe in one?"

"I say 'Divine Intelligence' more. Make more sense to me. Did Jesus call himself God?"

"He called himself the "Son of Man". He referred to "My Father in Heaven.""

"Son of Man, what means?"

"That he was both divine and human."

"He say that, or you say it?"

"I-I don't know."

The woman beside me stood up again. "In John 8:58 He says, "Before Abraham was born, I am."

"But what it means?"

Mrs. Smethens was standing very still and seemed frozen there for a few seconds. More murmuring behind me. "It's not for us to define it," she said at last. "It's a Divine Mystery, one of them."

"Ah, wery good. I think so, too. I think Divine Intelligence is the mystery. Too big for our mind to understand."

"Which is why we pray," she said, and sat down again.

From the back of the room someone called out, "Do you pray, Sir?"

"Every time," Rinpoche said.

"Every time what?" The person asked, and people laughed.

"Every time when I breathe. When I eat. When I, you know, go in the bathroom."

"Do you go to church, or just pray in the bathroom?" More laughter, subdued, mischievous. A little less polite now.

"Sometimes I go inside a church to pray. In Italy they had the beautiful churches and I went in and meditate there. Wery peaceful. You pray, too?"

"Daily," the person said, and the audience applauded him.

"Have you read the Bible?" Someone asked.

"Many time."

"Do you think it is the Word of God? Or the Word of the Divine Intelligence, as you would put it?"

"I like wery much the stories."

"The parables!" Four people shouted at once.

"Wery much. I like when they took the Jesus to arrested him they ask, "Who you say you are?" How he answer, do you know?"

"He didn't answer," a voice called from directly behind me. "He kept to a Divine silence in the face of evil."

Rinpoche nodded, smiled, but didn't speak. There seemed an obvious, pointed message in his silence, to me, at least. He ran his eyes across the crowd. If there had been a meter that measured the discomfort in that beautiful space, it would have been steadily creeping upward. Now it had started beeping at the top range, the red zone.

"Do you think you'll go to heaven?" someone called out.

"What is, this heaven?"

"We'll find out when we die!"

"I think," he said, "is a place not too much like this earth we live in. Here we have the killing, the raping, the war, the bad arguments one person against the next. I think, maybe, heaven does not have those things."

This remark brought a ringing round of applause, though I noticed that Professor Smethens beside me kept her hands folded in her lap.

"How we gonna get in that place, I think about now."

A voice behind me: "By good works, prayer, faith in Jesus Christ. By converting others to the true way."

Rinpoche pressed his lips together and very briefly looked at me. In that second he seemed almost in pain, but the trouble passed, and he swung his eyes up over the crowd. "'The Kingdom of Heaven is inside you,' Jesus said. What means?"

"That the Holy Spirit lives in us."

"How you know it?"

"We sense it in the quiet of our hearts!"

Rinpoche slowly folded his hands and seemed disinclined to say anything more.

"You never answered the question about God," a young man called out. "Was Jesus our Lord and Savior?"

"God was inside him," Rinpoche said—more applause. It was as if the assembled young people were cheering for the Jesus team, and it was winning. Bottom of the eighth, Jesus 8, the Enemy 1. I was hoping we could make it safely through the last few batters and get out of there, because, by then the awkwardness in the large, full auditorium had turned a corner into another feeling: a particular kind of bad energy, a mix of impatience, frustration, and something else, anger perhaps. The students weren't hearing exactly what they liked to hear from their invited guests. They didn't want the Devil to rally in the ninth. The key words seemed to be missing, and I sensed that both students and faculty were about to lose patience if Rinpoche didn't start speaking their language, talking about sinners and unfortunate agnostics, about salvation and souls and punishment and paradise. Beside me, Professor Smethens had taken to twisting her wedding ring, a nice diamond, around and around on her finger, very quickly.

"God is inside everything," Rinpoche said. "You know the adams?"

"Adam. Only one!" Someone yelled, to more laughter. "Adam and Eve!"

"No. I don't say it right. Adams. The molecoles. Inside everything."

"Atoms!" several people shouted. "Tuh, Tuh. T!"

"Yes! Maybe God is the adams and she is inside of everything that is. You, me, Jesus, this chair." He made a fist and pounded it lightly on the chair's wooden arm. "All the trees, the stones, the fishes, the stars. I think God is there, but in other shapes, different energies. But, not like a tree or a stone, only the human beings can make the adams go the good way or the bad."

"And what about sin?"

"Sin is hindrance," we say. "Keeps you from seeing God inside everything, inside everybody. Makes your mind like, like the eyeglasses with the mudge on them. If you want to see God in things, you have to clean the mudge!"

"Smudge," several students yelled at once. It had become a game, correcting the guest's pronunciation. The students were happy souls; it wasn't mocking laughter, but friendly in its own way, the way of Andalusia.

But then there was a sudden stirring at the end of my row and a man there sprang to his feet. Another faculty member, I assumed. "This is heresy!" he yelled out, and the atmosphere changed as suddenly as afternoon light on a lawn changes when a cloud blocks the sun. Until that moment, I'd had the sense that Rinpoche had won them over, even without using the key words. They liked him. Everyone always liked him. Almost everyone. When the word 'heresy' was spoken, a low chorus of "*booo*" sounded at the edges of the room. The faculty member went on, emboldened. "You, Sir, are our invited guest," he said, "so I won't insult you. But I feel you've insulted us! This is a sacred space, a *Christian* space. We can't have people likening Christ Jesus to *atoms,* of all things."

"You tell him, Mr. Jens!" someone shouted from the other side of the room.

And then two more voices: "Heresy!"

Mr. Jens was fortyish, with the build of a gym teacher, a head as bald as Rinpoche's, and tortoise-shell eyeglasses perched on a large, rather bulbous nose. He was standing tall with his hands on his hips, leaning slightly forward, scowling. A true believer.

Rinpoche watched him for a moment then said, "Why you angry on me?"

"Because you're bringing heretical ideas into contact with the minds of our Christian students, that is why, Sir."

A few quick bursts of applause sprouted here and there behind me. "Jens! Jens! Jens!" some students chanted, and then it caught on and knocked loudly against the walls. "Jens!"

Mr. Jens raised an arm to quiet them, and they fell silent immediately. "I think we've heard enough from you, Sir. I regret being part of the committee that invited you, even though I was the sole dissenting voice. I hope and pray the Lord God has mercy on you and converts you to the pure road."

Rinpoche watched him. Instinctively, the students quieted, as if to give him a last word, or as if hoping for a continuation of the argument. "Was Jesus only loving the Christians?" he asked. "Even because there were no Christians then?"

"The others shall be sent into eternal damnation, Sir! If that isn't clear from the Bible, nothing is!"

"I think is clear that maybe you have a lot of the anger inside you."

"Only in the presence of sin and blasphemy. And I think you've said quite enough."

Rinpoche didn't move, and, in the face of his interlocutor, held to what I thought of as a divine silence. I could see the student who'd introduced him sidestepping in toward center stage, watching Mr. Jens for clues as she went. Bravely, she said, "If there are no further questions, we have arranged for a nice reception for Mr. Rinpoch in the Langering Room afterwards. Everyone is welcome." One second of indecision and then the sounds of seats banging against seat backs, voices, footsteps.

Against a background of three hundred students standing up and walking toward the exits, I said to Professor Smethens, both of us standing, "Well, that was a good time."

She smirked.

"Where is the Langering Room?"

She flapped a hand toward the front left corner of the auditorium and turned and walked away.

I'd like to report that a great crowd of curious students headed in that direction. I'd also like to report that the Langering Room, with its long table covered with what was a wonderfully generous buffet of pastries, fruit, and pitchers of what appeared to be red fruit punch, was crowded with people who wanted to speak with the guest. But the room was, in fact, all but empty. The emptiness bothered the young chaperone more than it bothered me, and bothered me more than it bothered Rinpoche, who was happily pouring himself a paper cup of the punch and delicately placing slices of pineapple onto a plate, as if there were some other guest for whom it had all been arranged. I walked over to him. He looked up and smiled and said, "Wery nice people!"

"Really?"

A shrug. "One man little angry with me. Mr. Jents."

"That exchange didn't bother you?"

"Bother him, not me, Otto. I'm the same that I was."

"You did a nice job."

"Thank you. I like the pineapples."

At that moment I came to an understanding of what I had seen and sensed the night before, that strange connection between Andalusia and Rinpoche. They were both, in their own way, innocent, doubtless, hard to fluster, and Rinpoche had instinctively found that common territory with her. The difference, to my way of thinking at least, was that Rinpoche's innocence was like pure spring water flowing out of the earth, and Andalusia's was like distilled water in a bottle on a pharmacy shelf. His seemed to come from within, and hers from without, something manufactured, even a bit forced. His way seemed extremely broad and all-embracing, and hers narrowed by the teaching of severe judgment. I couldn't imagine Rinpoche saying something like, "Unfortunately, my friend is an agnostic." I saw a pair of coffee urns at the end of the table, regular and decaf, and had stepped over there and poured myself a cup of the strong stuff when the door opened. I turned and saw Andalusia striding into the room accompanied by a young man and young woman. She shot me a big smile and went up to Rinpoche and said, "Can I hug you!"

Without hesitation, Rinpoche set down his paper plate and wrapped her in a warm embrace. She introduced her friends, "My name is actually Adam!" the young man said brightly. I didn't catch the young woman's name because by then Adam was saying, "You're a mystic! Your understanding of Christ Jesus is a mystical understanding, isn't it?"

"I don't know," Rinpoche told him.

"The perfect answer, a perfect Christ-like humility!" Adam turned and beamed at Andalusia, who was smiling at him proudly, as if to say, "See!"

The other young woman stood half a pace behind and to the side, shy, uncertain, watchful.

"Mr. Jens can be a little, you know, *rough!*" Andalusia said.

Adam piped up, "He toughens us for the battle against Satan."

Rinpoche nodded in a noncommittal way.

Adam turned to me. "You're his chaperone?"

"Brother-in-law. Friend," I said. And then, for some reason, "Spiritual student."

"And the two nicest people who ever came into the restaurant!" Andalusia said. "They gave me money and I put it in the charity box, to help the poor! Well, we have to get to class. They didn't time this right. I'm sure lots of people would have come, but class starts in eight minutes. It was so exciting to have a real Buddhist here, to listen to something so different and yet so . . ."

"Reverent," the shy young woman put in. She held out a notebook to Rinpoche. "Can I get your autograph?"

The good monk obliged. They all shook his hand, wished him 'a blessed day', and I watched them go happily back out into their clean world.

Roland Merullo

"Wery nice people," Rinpoche said to me again.

The chaperone approached him, thanked him for his "fascinating talk" and handed him a white envelope. "Your honorarium," she said.

But Rinpoche wouldn't take it from her. "I have enough of the money now," he said. "I want that you give it to the man who was angry on me, Mr. Jents, and ask him if he can make something nice for the students. Bring here someone who makes music, maybe. Some food. Making them happy."

"We have a budget for that already, Mr. Rinpoch."

"Good, good. Make the budget bigger! And now my friend and me we have to go. I want to see my nephew! My favorite one!" Rinpoche laughed, hooked an arm around my neck, and pulled me close. "Son of man!" he said. "This man!"

The hug wasn't gentle. A few drops off coffee spilled onto the toe of my right running shoe.

"Thank you for having me to talk," he said to the young woman. "Have a blessed day."

By that point, the poor chaperone seemed to have exhausted herself, whipsawed as she was between her official duties and some sense that a dire reprimand awaited her when the heretics had left campus. I worried she'd have to face some kind of disciplinary action for her role in the day's debacle, if it had been, in fact, a debacle. I tried to imagine her giving the check and the message to Mr. Jens, what his reaction would be, who would bear his anger. But she was leading us out of the building into the sunlight, thanking Rinpoche, apologizing, confused. And then the two of us were free and heading over to the beautiful truck. From across the campus someone yelled, "Thank you! God Bless!" in a cheery voice. Rinpoche and I each raised an arm in an identical gesture, and we were on the road again.

Twenty-Two

According to Google Maps, it is exactly 206.5 miles from the Liberty University campus in Lynchburg, Virginia, to the office building where Anthony works, in Charlotte, North Carolina. Once we made our escape from Greater Lynchburg, the good monk and I headed south on a mostly empty Route 29, through hilly, wooded territory. I have a fascination with roadside signs—they often speak volumes about the territory—and Route 29 didn't disappoint in that regard. There was a ten-foot-by-four-foot TRUMP 2024 sign in front of one very modest home along that route, and other signs for The Virginia Whiskey Experience Museum, Sweet Briar College, and a place named Hurt, Virginia. A little way down the road from Hurt I spotted a large LET'S GO BRANDON flag, something I didn't even try to explain to Rinpoche. Then a lawn sign advertising an Extreme Bull Bash. A large, tattered Confederate flag flying by the highway north of Danville.

Just across the line into North Carolina we spotted this message in front of a church: "Purge me with hyssop, and I shall be clean." (Hyssop, I would later learn, is a medicinal herb, often used as an expectorant).

I was grateful that Rinpoche didn't ask about these various messages. So much of America—of any society—is difficult to explain to a non-native. To ease the monotony in the months before I sold the house, I fell into the habit of doing the Times

171

crossword puzzle every day, an activity I'd enjoyed in my youth and then given up in the busy years of child-rearing. The crossword answers included everything from baseball trivia to the stage names of sitcom stars, from nicknames for cities to slang terms like "hang five" and "buzzed". How was a Tibetan-Siberian, how was any non-American-raised puzzler, supposed to know such things?

Rinpoche was quiet in the passenger seat, hands folded in his lap, his head turning at times to follow the passing scenery: horses in a corral; a vineyard with neat rows of vines; kindergarteners spilling out of a school bus and running toward a waiting parent, knapsacks bouncing and dragging. I knew my brother-in-law well enough by then to know that he didn't want to rehash the speaking engagement.

I was buried in my own thoughts, and some of them were so disturbing that I could have used a little hyssop. We passed ramshackle houses with piles of junk in the front yard, and that hint of Appalachian poverty, along with the political signs, the enormous Confederate flag, and the echoes of Mr. Jens yelling "Heresy!" put me in a certain mood. In my own way, I decided, I wasn't so different from Andalusia. She wanted people to be 'saved'; I wanted them to be happy. Or at least at peace, not hungry, not poor in the richest nation in the history of mankind, not so furiously at odds with one another. I wanted America to be a nation where the well-fed would look out for the hungry, the wealthy would look out for the poor, the calm would look out for the troubled. That desire was at the heart of what Tom had called "The Giving Project": I wanted to spread a few small seeds of happiness along the route of our trip, to revive a hotel maid's faith in humanity by leaving her a hundred-dollar bill, for example.

Along those stretches of Highway 29 where we could see only the rolling hills and streams and forests and pastures of northwestern North Carolina—no political signs, no religious exhortations, no advertisements—the world seemed peaceful and simple, time passing steadily through the God-atoms of creation. "You're a mystic!" Adam had said of Rinpoche, and that was true. A mystic was able to focus on something larger than the contentious minutiae of the daily whirl. A mystic wouldn't hang a LET'S GO BRANDON, FJB sign in front of his or her house, or be upset at seeing such a message. I wanted that view, that kind of engaged but untroubled consciousness. I wanted to be in the world but not of it.

Rinpoche had shown that level of consciousness to me, in the flesh, shown me that it was not merely an abstract possibility. Once I'd gotten over my initial suspicion of him, and my initial resistance to his way of being, I sensed in myself a deeply buried desire for that larger view. And now, after years of his tutelage, I felt, at times, fleetingly, that he'd brought me into at least the outskirts of that realm. But the way my mind had worked at Liberty University showed me that I was still mired in judgment. I had no doubt that Rinpoche would share some of those judgments. I knew he'd never fly a Confederate flag, for instance; he had a pretty good idea what it meant. I doubted he'd ever accuse someone of heresy. But, in his case, it was as if a much larger mind stood behind those judgments, as if he could hold them all in a perspective I lacked. *Love* was the word for that perspective. Without speaking aloud, I said, to the famous Mr. Jens, "If that isn't clear from the Bible, nothing is. If love wasn't the point of Jesus's preaching and actions, nothing was."

We stopped in the pleasant town of Greensboro, North Carolina, scene of the famous Woolworth Counter sit-ins which, in 1960, had propelled much of the Civil Rights movement. The building had now been turned into a museum. We strolled the city's wide, busy main street. We enjoyed a very fine snack of coffee and scones at an establishment called Green Bean on Elm. After that short break, standing on a street corner waiting for the light to change, we found ourselves beside a middle-aged couple, and I struck up a conversation. A brother and sister, it turned out, she a resident, he a visitor. When they asked why we were in Greensboro, I said something about escaping the end of a long northern winter, and she said, and I swear this is true, "We moved down here from near Boston just for that reason. It's great. The people are friendly, the winters are mild."

"Where, near Boston?"

"A place called Revere," she said. "Dale Street. Do you know it?"

"The nice beach!" Rinpoche said, and his words made the woman happy, you could see it. Her brother, a bit rough around the edges, tattoos up his forearms, tattered, sleeveless motorcycle jacket hugging strong shoulders, said little at first, seemed very shy, and then: "I'm Buddhist. I know who you are, Rinpoche. I have every single one of your books, and they've changed my life."

"You a good person," Rinpoche said. "Anybody sees it."

By that point in my travels with Rinpoche, I'd stopped being surprised by what seemed impossible coincidences, and stopped being surprised when people recognized him on the street. But, surprise or no, that small moment lifted me free of the dark swirls of my negative mood. The brother and sister seemed like happy people, and their quiet, contagious happiness reminded me of a rare piece of fatherly advice I'd given Natasha when she first went away to her high-powered, Ivy

League college. I told her not to worry too much about success and status, even though she'd be surrounded by brilliant and ambitious peers who were determined to improve the world. "Be happy in whatever you do," I said, "and you'll change the world with every interaction you ever have."

Rinp and I parted ways with the couple and, a little further up the block, stopped to let one of the longest freight trains on earth cross the main drag. Bells dinging, black-and-white arms swinging, the whistle, the clacking, graffiti-splattered cars, scores of them, loaded mainly with coal and oil. As we waited, a small brown-and-white dog, held on its leash by a woman about thirty, came up and nuzzled Rinpoche's bare ankle. He reached down to pet it, and when the train had passed and the dog and its owner had moved on, he said to me, as casually as someone else might have spoken about the weather, or the train, or the coffee, "Most of dogs are bodhisattvas, Otto."

Some brothers-in-law, too, I thought, and we found the pickup safe and shining in the lot opposite Greensboro's big new police station, and headed south for a meeting with my beloved son.

175

Twenty-Three

For one piece of the short leg from Greensboro to Charlotte, Rinpoche took the wheel, keeping the truck at 60 mph and focusing intently. Near Salisbury, with a light rain falling, we stopped to fill the tank and switched places. In Boston, New York, and D.C., we'd still see people wearing the facemasks that had been mandatory in so many places at the height of the pandemic, but the farther south we drove, the more noses and mouths we saw. By then, a million Americans had died of Covid, and the nation, already divided, had been divided again between those who thought the bacterium was a lethal threat and those who did not, those who'd lined up anxiously for the vaccine, and those who, for various reasons, avoided and dismissed it. Like so many others, I tried to penetrate to the heart of this divisiveness, tried to comprehend how we'd become a country of arguers, taking furious stands on everything from vaccination to school textbooks. Bronxville was very liberal and North Dakota very conservative, and the conversations I heard in those two places might as well have been carried on in two different languages. Friends of mine blamed a recent presidency for that division, and I mostly agreed. But I was old enough—if barely—to remember the division over the war in Vietnam, a division that continued long after the American involvement there had ended. And then, of course, there had been the much greater division in 1860. Families had been torn asunder then. The same thing was happening now, and one of the reasons I was thinking about this disharmony on the ride to Charlotte was because a version of that disharmony had infected my own family.

Our children, Natasha and Anthony, both highly educated, both fine people, held very different political views and had chosen very different routes into adulthood. Tasha had left Brown to care for her dying mother, and then, instead of returning for her junior year, as I'd hoped, she'd moved to North Dakota to live with Seese and Rinpoche and help out with the meditation retreats there. She devoted her time to that work, to her own meditation and yoga practices, to gardening, and to certain groups involved in environmental activism. She'd become a vegetarian, dressed simply, owned next to nothing, and she'd told me, more than once—as if she'd taken my fatherly advice and added another dimension to it—that what mattered to her in life wasn't money and career, but what she called an 'interior purification', a kind of preparation for 'the other world.' Seese told me that Tasha had maintained, for years now, her love interest out there on the Dakotan plains, an older guy from a local family, someone who saw the world as she did and eschewed the frantic climb up the ladder of material and professional success that consumed so many members of their generation—and my own.

Anthony could not have been more different. He'd played football at Bowdoin, and, after graduation, had moved to Manhattan with two of his teammates and taken a job on Wall Street. I'd never understood exactly what he did there, only that he worked for a firm owned by an older Bowdoin alum, that he spent long hours in the office, and that he seemed happy. After four years in New York, he and his closest college friend moved to Charlotte, and went to work for a hedge fund called Redder Mountain Capital Investment Group. Anthony had always been less communicative than his sister, but we spoke by phone once a month or so. Whenever I asked him to tell me about his work, he'd say things like, "We just move money around, Dad, that's all." Or, "We make rich people richer and try to get richer ourselves." From time to time I'd receive a postcard from one exotic destination or another—a Caribbean island, the south of France, a fancy Hawaiian resort—and, though it often seemed he was traveling with a female companion, when I inquired, gently, about his love life, the answers would be similarly evasive, "Just playing the field, Dad. Sowing the oats, you know. Having fun."

As he edged into his thirties, I kept hoping, as I did with Natasha—my own bias, I suppose, having enjoyed family life—that Anthony would find a woman he loved, maybe consider marriage and kids. I didn't voice those hopes, of course. Jeannie and I had made a point of never urging our children in any particular direction, offering, instead of career and life advice, a steady love and support.

I'd read the articles about young adults of my kids' generation waiting longer to marry, sometimes eschewing marriage altogether, about the preference many of them exhibited for career over children. I understood that perfectly well. But I confess to worrying, at times, that Jeannie's premature death had been a crushing blow to my children's sense of family life. *What good was it,* I imagined them thinking, *what's the point of creating a small, loving group in a home you care for when all of it can be demolished with a diagnosis?!*

So, as the Charlotte skyline rose into view against a gray sky, I could feel a particular kind of anxiety gnawing at my entrails. I loved my son. I was pleased at his success. I never expected him to make meditation the center of his life, the way Natasha, Seese, and Rinpoche had done. There were other ways to develop one's spiritual life, and certainly other ways to contribute to humanity. I didn't know enough about Anthony's work to judge it one way or another, but I had the nagging sense—I'd had it to varying degrees for years—that we were growing apart, he and I, that the same dirty wedge that was splitting American society into two distant camps, had sliced into the tissue of my family life. That life, that love, had been the heart of my world, the part of existence that had enabled me to survive what I'd had to cope with over the past decade: loss of spouse, loss of career, aging, change. I remembered with a great, tender vividness, the meals the four of us had enjoyed around the table of the house in Bronxville, the backyard barbecues with our kids' grade school, high school, and college friends, the vacation trips, the times spent sprawled on various pieces of living room furniture, laughing at a sitcom or TV film, the sporting events and plays and a capella concerts and birthday parties, the Thanksgiving and Christmas celebrations, the magical sense of unity that had glued us so tightly together even as Natasha and Anthony went off to college and began the sometimes treacherous movement into their own adult lives.

I'd told Anthony that we didn't want to interrupt him at work, that we'd have a meal together instead, take a walk, sit around his apartment or our hotel room for a few hours, catching up. But he'd said no, he wanted us to see his office. "No problem, Dad. Whenever you get here is fine. Park in the garage under the building and just come on up."

We found the address, dipped down into the garage, parked there, checked in at a security desk, rode the elevator to the 23rd floor, and stepped through a glass door into the splendid offices of The Redder Mountain Capital Investment Group.

A gloriously beautiful young woman sat at a desk facing us. Long red hair, shining, pale eyes, perfect skin. I thought for a moment that we'd accidentally wandered into a modeling agency. "Can I help you?" Her desk was immaculate. On the walls hung large, framed photographs of spectacular natural scenes—hundred-foot waterfalls, snow-dusted gray mountains, desert dunes. Behind her, huge windows, spotted with raindrops, looked out on the Charlotte skyline. A young man walked past behind her. White shirt and tie, no sport coat, no belly, he moved like a professional martial arts master or Yankee shortstop. Not a modeling agency then, a spa of some kind, a fitness center, a futuristic world in which everyone stood at the apex of the human pyramid. "Can I help you gentlemen?" the young woman asked again. "I'm Chantelle." Perfectly trained, Chantelle did not let her eyes wander over Rinpoche's robe or my tattered, coffee-stained running shoes, but I felt the way I'd felt when I'd first stepped into a Manhattan job interview, fresh from the North Dakota wilds. I was a rube again, a bumpkin who'd taken a wrong turn and stumbled into the heaven realm. I almost apologized.

"Uh, my son," I said.

Chantelle gazed at me calmly, expectantly.

"Anthony Ringling. My son works here. We've come to see him. He should be expecting—"

"Dad! Rinp!" I heard, and Anthony was at the door of the glass-walled office to our right, a citizen of this magical realm, tall, well built, stylish haircut, wide shoulders covered by an expensive-looking suit jacket. "Chantelle, this is my dad and my uncle, great men!"

He came over and, instead of hugging us, shook our hands, then turned us, with one hand on my upper back and one on Rinp's, and led us into the glass-walled office. "Man," he exclaimed, "it's like medicine to see you both. Like actual medicine!"

Anthony closed the door behind us—a soft *click*—gestured for Rinpoche and me to take two of the leather chairs around a low, circular, glass-topped table, and he took the third. Once he left adolescence behind, my son had become one of the best-organized human beings I knew ("Neat freak" was Natasha's term for it), and his office was without blemish. A large wooden desk was backed by floor-to-ceiling windows that offered a view across the city. On the walls hung three framed photos behind glass: scenes of southwest North Dakota, a part of the state that resembled the Grand Canyon. Natasha had taken those photos, and it both pleased and stung me to see them there. Pleased me, because my children were no longer particularly close to each other, and here, perhaps, was a sign of rapprochement. Natasha had made a gift of them to her brother, and her brother had thought enough of the gift to mount the photos and hang them on his office walls.

The sting came from the fact that Jeannie had been a photographer, and it was only after her death—possibly *because* of her death—that making pictures had become a passion for our daughter.

The three of us had been sitting there only a matter of seconds, only long enough for me to make a quick perusal of the office, when the door opened and the gorgeous Chantelle appeared with a tray on which stood three glasses of lemon water on ice. Wordlessly, she set them in front of us, and I was glad, for some strange reason, to see on her left forearm an oval birthmark about the size of an egg and the color of an eggshell. It pleased me, I think, odd duck that I am, because from the moment we'd stepped through the door, I felt we'd entered a realm scrubbed free of even the smallest imperfection, a futuristic world from which messy desks and scuffed shoes had been banished. Chantelle smiled and left us—another soft *click*.

"You're looking great," I said to Anthony, which was true. Before sitting down, he'd taken off his suit jacket and hung it on a hook, and even with the white dress shirt and blue silk tie, you could see in what fine condition he kept himself. Clean-shaven cheeks, his mother's piercing green eyes, dark brown hair swept back and neatly parted, he'd never looked better.

"Thanks, Pop," he said. "Cool footwear."

I looked down at my less-than-new running shoes. "Retirement," I said.

"Maybe we wessle now?" Rinpoche suggested, moving to the edge of his seat as if he were about to stand and renew their decades-long Greco-Roman style competition.

Anthony laughed, a bit uncomfortably it seemed, and sipped from his glass of lemon water. "Nah, man," he said, setting down the glass and turning his hands in toward himself. "This shirt and tie together cost around four hundred bills."

"My robe is sacred Robe," Rinpoche said, imitating the hand gesture.

"Right, Rinp. But you'd have me on the ground in two seconds and your robe wouldn't suffer at all. Plus, I have to maintain a serious demeanor, you know, so I don't make the clients uneasy. They're putting a *lot* of money in my hands. If one of them happened to come in and see me wrestling with my uncle the famous monk, and losing besides, it wouldn't inspire confidence."

Rinpoche sat back, smiling, as if it had all been a joke anyway. "What you doing with their money. Seese explain me many time. I never understood it."

Anthony glanced up above our heads, just for a second, through the glass wall and into the office. I wondered if he might be looking at Chantelle. "I protect it, Rinp. We move it here and there, making sure it gets bigger over time, not smaller."

"What happens if gets smaller? Means they are hungry, the people?"

Anthony laughed again and shook his head. "Not likely. Means two weeks in Telluride at Christmas instead of four. Means a little less help in the Naples beach house, or a smaller yacht. That kind of thing. Means sharing a private plane instead of owning one."

"Lot of pressure?" I asked.

"Day and night, Pop. It's why I make the big bucks."

"But you're happy?"

"Great apartment. Best restaurant meals. Gatsbyesque parties. And a parade of fabulous women. No complaints."

Something sour was in the air then, just a hint of it curling around my face like the scent of sulphur from a lit match. "And a great view!" I managed, then brought the glass to my mouth. I tried to keep my thoughts from showing, and swung my eyes to one of Tasha's photos. The idea that Anthony—always such a caring child—carrying geckos across the road to they wouldn't be squashed, giving away a quarter of his summer earnings to a local women's shelter—should be working eighty hours a week so someone could keep a large yacht, fed my judgmental side, I admit. But what troubled me more was the sense that he'd been infected by a certain slight artificiality. He seemed to be playing a role, copying someone—a boss or former boss, a partner. I was glad about the exciting lifestyle—not a terrible way to enter your thirties, though Jeannie and I had chosen a different route. But this was my son; I could see past the gleaming surfaces, the four-hundred-dollar shirt and tie, and into the center of him. Some former Anthony was squirming there. He leaned back, crossed one leg over the other, ankle to knee, and flipped the tassel on his loafers a few times. "You were married at my age, Pop," he said. "You don't know how exhausting the dating life can be. Decent single guys with money are like rock stars in this town! I don't get enough sleep!"

I produced a smile. I could feel Rinpoche watching both of us. "Rinp spoke at Liberty University this morning," I said.

Anthony turned his head. "Seriously, Unc?! I wouldn't have figured that as a winning market for you."

"Wery nice people!"

Anthony laughed someone else's laugh. An alien chuckle. "Everybody's very nice people for you, Unc. Who isn't very nice people in your book?"

"Putin," Rinpoche said immediately.

"Yeah. Now there's a true shitshow. He's making the markets go insane." Another glance into the office. "Speaking of shitshows . . . what's this Aunt Seese tells me, Pop? You're giving away our money?"

"Just the house proceeds. Most of them. I put a fair sum-"

"*Just,* Pop! *Just* the house proceeds?! I could have doubled that for you in five years. What were you thinking?"

"I was thinking we have enough."

The alien laugh again. "Not a word we use around here, Pop. *Enough.* Not a great word, man."

The other not-great words that crawled up from my throat into my mouth at that moment were: *What happened to you?* But I bit down on them. My own father had said those exact words to me when he realized I didn't envision a future farming the land he and his father had farmed, that I was intending to settle, not in North Dakota, but in New York City, and that I was going to make a living editing food books. Our relationship, such as it was, had never recovered from that remark—*What happened to you, Otto?*—and the ugly conversation that followed. I didn't want to rule Anthony's life with my judgments and criticisms, with my ideas of the best way to live. Maybe he'd get to be my age and give away millions. Plus, I knew what had happened to him. I didn't need to ask. His mother had died when he was not yet twenty. And all he'd ever been able to say to that was *No! No! No! No!* For two seconds then it seemed to me that everything from the artificial laugh to the eighty-hour work weeks could be traced to that *No!* All of it was a frantic attempt to shove the thought of death into a sack and hide the sack in a cellar corner.

I felt a surge of the purest love for him then.

He looked at the glass wall and made a gesture to someone on the other side of it—one hand raised, thumb and index finger half an inch apart. *Be there shortly.*

"We don't want to keep you," I said, taking my cue. "What time's good for dinner?"

Anthony flexed his cheeks, cleared his throat. "Oh, Pop, I can't do dinner. I'll be here til eight-thirty or nine and then I have a kind of, you know, date. Hottest date on earth."

"Oh," I said. "All right. Breakfast then?"

"I'm at the gym at five, Pop, here by six-thirty."

Anthony was standing. Rinpoche and I stood. From a jar on his desk my son took two thick cigars. "But these," he said, handing one to each of us, "will more than make up for my absence. I'm coming to New York in a month, we'll do dinner then. On me. You pick the spot."

We won't be in New York then, I started to say, but Anthony was putting on his suit jacket and ushering us out, palms on our backs. He shook my hand with a firm grip and excellent eye contact, thanked me for coming, "I wanted you to see this place," he said. He hugged Rinpoche, said, "Love ya, Unc," and then, somehow, before I could say or do anything else, Chantelle, smiling, saying how 'fantastic' it had been to have met Mr. Ringling's father and uncle, was leading us to the exit.

185

Twenty-Four

Rinpoche and I drove in a terrible silence from Anthony's office to the inn Seese had found for us in a nearby neighborhood of fine brick homes and shrubbery. The silence was terrible for me, at least. Rinpoche sat quietly in the passenger seat, twirling both unlit cigars in his fingers and studying the city streets. I struggled to understand what I was feeling. I suppose part of the emotion came from the fact that, like so many new 'converts' to a certain spiritual path, I wanted company. Rinpoche had guided me into a serious meditation practice, a practice that appealed to Seese and Tasha, too, and one that had made me care less about money, be less afraid of getting old and dying, be more aware of myself and the world. And so, naturally perhaps, foolishly perhaps, I wanted those same things for my son. But the more I pondered my feelings, the more it seemed to me that it wasn't so much what Anthony was doing for work that bothered me (I knew that hedge funds existed not only to make rich people richer, but sometimes to protect the endowment of a university or a charitable foundation) but the observation that he seemed inauthentic, as if, over the years since college, he'd been carefully crafting another personality. Even that wasn't so bad: people changed as they aged. I didn't want him to be the teenage Anthony or the college Anthony for the rest of his life. But my intuitive sense was that this inauthenticity was an armor. Against death, perhaps.

186

Against the softness in him, the vulnerability. His mother's passing had crushed him, and the more I thought about it, the clearer it seemed that he was building a fortress against his own deepest feelings so that he'd never be hurt that way again.

Whatever the actual reason, I was enveloped in sadness by the time we found the Morehead Inn and pulled into its gravel lot. The inn was a white-sided old southern mansion, replete with magnificent downstairs sitting rooms, chandeliers, oriental carpets, a dining room, and a library with soft chairs and three little birds flitting here and there in a glass box. Australian finches, the woman who greeted us said they were, gorgeous creatures about the size of a sparrow and colored in vibrant greens and golds. Rinpoche stood in front of the glass box, transfixed. It was as if a vapor was emanating from his whole body, appreciation for their beauty, compassion for their imprisonment. The woman who'd greeted us coughed discreetly, or Rinp might have stayed there like that for half an hour.

We were led upstairs to separate rooms, each with a four-poster bed and a divan, curtained windows, tiled bath, old-fashioned, high-backed armchairs, and lamps on small bureaus. At the door of my room, Rinpoche put a hand on my shoulder and said, "Rest now, Otto. Later we go out for food, okay?"

I took off my running shoes and lay face-up on the bedspread. There was a tiny crack in the ceiling plaster directly above me, a thin, crooked, wandering line. It looked like a river of darkness against the pearly background. Years earlier, Rinpoche had taught me a magical Tibetan meditation called *tonglen,* sometimes called 'the meditation of giving and taking.' The practice involves taking on someone else's suffering and distress with the in-breath, then giving them love, peace, health, joy, and comfort, on the out-breath. It can be done for an individual, a group of people, the world at large, or for oneself, and can include only a few breaths or an hour or more of 'giving and taking.' When he'd first described it to me, I thought *tonglen* sounded simplistic, almost a superstition: as if matching certain thoughts to my breathing might actually erase so much as one second of suffering from this earth. In time, however, I came to see the magic in it, the way it could transmute the thought process and change how I felt about someone, or a group of people, or myself. Alone in the Bronxville house during the hardest months, I'd made *tonglen* the focus of my meditations two or three times a week. I did *tonglen* for Jeannie's spirit, for Tasha and Anthony, for a neighbor's yapping dogs, for hospital patients, abandoned children, hungry sub-Saharans—any creature or group that happened to come to mind. At Rinpoche's suggestion, I started doing *tonglen* for myself on Saturday mornings, imagining myself as a separate being, taking the loneliness and sorrow from that being, and breathing out strength and peace. I can honestly say that, once I overcame my initial skepticism, I never stood up from a *tonglen* meditation without feeling better about the world and a bit more confident in my ability to endure difficulties and give comfort.

So I set the alarm on my phone and spent half an hour on the bed in the Morehead Inn doing a *tonglen* meditation for my son, taking from him the fear, bitterness, and pain I'd sensed there, buried beneath the glittering lifestyle. On the out-breath I 'gave' him a quietly shimmering interior world, a reflection of his uncle's spirit, a lake surface with no ripples disturbing it, a pearly ceiling with no cracks.

I will say only this: the ancient Tibetan sages might have been incapable of designing and building a thirty-story office building or tailoring a four-hundred-dollar shirt and tie combo, but they understood something about the human mind and spirit that the brightest Western scholars have yet to grasp.

I showered and changed clothes and met my teacher downstairs in the library. We sat close to each other in two armchairs and talked for a while.

"You a little sad, Otto," Rinpoche said. And I admitted that I was and told him that the *tonglen* session had helped.

He nodded and smiled. "Anthony so happy to show you his work. So proud for his father to see it."

"I know. He just doesn't seem true to himself anymore."

"Maybe," Rinpoche admitted, running his gaze over bookshelves filled with old volumes no one seemed to have touched since the Civil War. He brought his eyes back to me and said, "In the East we say if somebody sleeping, don't wake him up. Let him wake up when the time come."

"Right. I just, I don't know, I love him so much and he seems like he's *pretending* to be happy, like he's learned the definition of happiness from outside himself, and is acting for some other set of eyes."

"Maybe."

"In some way, I don't think he's ever come to terms with Jeannie's death."

"Hard, losing the mother."

"Right. I know. Hard for all of us, even after all this time. I want to put my arms around him and say it will be all right. That his mother would want him not to keep mourning. I feel like he's encased in a shiny suit, not an actual suit, but a suit of personality that belongs to somebody else, that's there as a protection. Do you know what I mean?"

Rinpoche nodded again, as solemn a gesture as I'd ever seen from him. "He didn't want to wessle me."

"I get that. He's in his office, all dressed up and everything. He would have looked foolish. But the fact that he couldn't make time to have dinner with us, or even breakfast. . . . That hurt."

Another solemn nod. "You don't always know how many chances you gonna have to see somebody."

"Exactly. But he seems to have taken the opposite lesson from Jeannie's passing."

"Doesn't want to think on it. When he seeing us, he has to think on it, about his mother. So if he has the dinner or breakfast with us, it remind him."

I drew in a long breath and let it out. More or less back to where I'd been, mentally, before the visit to Redder Mountain Capital, I reached for that rectangular savior, the iPhone, and swiped through, looking for places we might have dinner. "Ever had Ethiopian food?" I asked Rinpoche.

"Not one time."

"Willing to give it a try?"

"Sure, Otto."

I plugged the address into Google Maps, we went outside to the truck, and Rinpoche held the phone as we headed out in a light rain. I'd never spent time in Charlotte, and it wasn't easy to get a sense of the place as I drove. The rain, two separate construction detours, a small highway, the confident directions in that strangely mechanized female voice, and then at last we saw a sign for Abugida Ethiopian Café and Restaurant. A good meal, I was thinking, a cuisine I don't know well, and, with the *tonglen* and Rinpoche's words, I'd be fully healed. But, inside the small place we discovered that the kitchen had closed minutes earlier. "No chance?" I asked the woman at the desk. She smiled a lovely smile and shook her head.

Outside again, with the rain falling more forcefully now, I spotted a Vietnamese restaurant in a strip mall across the way—Pho Hoa.

We drove across the road and enjoyed a tasty meal there. A chicken Pho for me and a tofu Pho for my companion. "You're not eating much meat anymore, I noticed."

"Had enough meat in this life, Otto."

"And you're smoking cigars now, or at least you took one."

"We smoke them one time soon, you and me," was all he said.

"Now you're the one who seems sad."

"Only little bit. Little small, how you say, *insept* running in my thought stream now."

"Insect. About what? Anthony?"

"This a sad trip," he said. "War on the radio, the woman who had her husband die in Syria, the poor peoples, the hungry peoples, a little bit Anthony. Jeannie not here."

"I've infected you," I tried.

He shook his head. "Okay to be a little sad sometimes, Otto. Okay to maybe smoking the cigar one time, eating the meat a little, you know. Skip one day in meditation. Okay not to be the machine. Not perfect. Not hitting the middle circle with the hatch every time."

"Hatchet, yes. It was easy for you."

"Lot of things easy for me."

"Why?"

"Because I know my mind is why."

"Marriage was easy for me, almost always. Fatherhood was mostly easy. Work was easy. At the same time, though, in those years, I could never completely relax. There was always something—one of the kids was sick, or we had a stretch of money worries. Car trouble, house repair, world events. Always something. A tough day at work. The times leading up to and right after our parents died. Being let go from a job I liked, years before I was ready."

191

"Divine Intelligence shaking you so you don't fall asleep again. Gonna talk about that when I do the last talk."

I swirled the rice noodles around with the tips of the chopsticks, watching the way the short-lived eddy moved the broth and mint and bits of hot pepper. I could feel Rinpoche's eyes on me.

I looked up. "I've been thinking about this a lot lately, Rinp. I guess I've felt like I've made some *progress* in the meditative life, if that's the right word. My meditations, some of them at least, are quieter. I feel like I'm more patient than I used to be, that I can, I don't know, *endure* more than I used to be able to endure."

"What means?"

"Endure? It means bear. Deal with. Accept with equanimity. But I guess I also thought that, after years of practicing and reading and being with you, after some of those great meditations I had out west. . . . I don't know, I guess I hoped I wouldn't feel the negative things so strongly. Not that I'd be totally immune to sadness or disappointment or fear or any of that, but that those things wouldn't weigh on my as heavily. Wouldn't knock me flat."

"Like getting the waccine," he said. "You still get sick, but probably not so bad."

"Something like that. Meditation as a vaccine against the bad stuff."

Rinpoche pursed his lips, and I could see that he was thinking of a way to reach me, to provide another *wesson*. I watched him and waited.

"Seese has the arthritis," he said.

"I know. From my mother's family. That side was riddled with it. I was spared. I've always worried it would hit one of the kids."

"She takes the pills. A shot sometimes. Like a vaccine."

"I know."

"Makes the pain lesser. Doesn't take it all away."

I nodded, twirled my pho, looked up. Preoccupied as I was, replaying the visit with Anthony, it took me a moment to understand what he was getting at.

"The big whirl outside and the small whirl inside like a mirror, Otto. Some days sun, some days like today rain. Hot some days, then cold."

"The famous Yin-Yang," I said.

"Yes!" Apparently excited at that connection, Rinp removed one strand of thin noodle from his bowl and set it on the empty plate between us. Removed another noodle. Deftly working the tips of the chopsticks, he arranged the first noddle in a rough circle, then lifted the second into place, touched it here and there until he'd curved it the way he wanted, the two noodles forming the shape of the Yin-Yang: a circle with the S-curve along its middle. He carefully removed two small chips of the hot green pepper from the bottom of his bowl and placed one on each side.

"Nice," I said.

He held the chopsticks so the tips were touching and then ran them in the air just above the noodle that separated the two halves of the diagram. "This line," he said in his teaching voice, "is the place you go in meditation. Every time you sit, year after year, life after life, you resting on this line. Pretty soon you stay there, like the big masters."

"Pretty soon?"

He laughed. "Maybe not *soon* like you thinking about it. Maybe a hundred lifes."

"Great."

"Sometime," he moved the points to one side then the other, "you go over here for a little while, maybe one day, one year, one life or ten lifes for some people in hell realm. Sometime you go over the other side, everything good, happy, good body, good money, food, love. Heaven realm. You want to stay in there, everybody wants to. But the world turns over every day," he lifted his free hand and made circles with his index finger. "Time goes. You get old. People you love dies. Changes, changes, changes. But this line, if you stay there, on it, you feel like you have the adams of the God inside you. Adams, yes?"

"Atoms. A 't' but it sounds like a 'd'."

"And those kind of changes don't hurt you so much. So forever now, whenever you sad, look for this middle place inside you. I know you have it. Look for it, and the sadness becomes like one star in the sky far away, see?"

"I think so, yes. Thank you."

"Welcome."

Rinpoche then leaned his face down toward the plate and, moving this way and that, daintily sucked the noodly Yin-Yang diagram into his mouth. He smacked his lips, he laughed. He picked up the chips of pepper with the chopsticks, placed them into his mouth, swallowed, and bathed me in a huge smile. While this odd performance was taking place, our waiter had approached, about to ask about dessert. You guys save any room for some caramel flan? Bubble tea? When I looked up at him—he hadn't quite reached our table—he noticed Rinpoche's antics, then grinned and said, "That good, huh?" and my brother-in-law laughed one of his infectious laughs, at himself, at life, at this fearful world.

Twenty-Five

Breakfast at the Morehead Inn was served in a narrow, elegant dining room that occupied one corner of the old mansion. Windows along two sides of the room let in a muted but promising March sunlight, as if the summer were saying, quietly, "I'm coming, I'm coming. Be there soon. Keep the faith." The table was beautifully set; the morning light reflected in sparkling water glasses and on the dishes and cutlery and even in the bouquets of flowers in tall vases in the corners. Rinpoche and I had completed our regular morning meditation in my room, then ambled downstairs on the early side, drawn by the delicious kitchen smells. The only other guests at that hour were a couple about my age—tall man in a long-sleeved golf jersey, short woman in a bright dress—who arrived a few seconds before us and took the chairs on the side opposite. All four of us eschewed the egg dishes and ordered pancakes and coffee from a young woman who told us her name was Elsa. While we waited for the food to be served, the female half of the couple opposite us eyed Rinpoche's maroon robe and asked where we were from.

"Siberia," Rinpoche said, before I had a chance to offer a different response.

"No kidding!" the man boomed out in a bass voice that made the water glasses wobble. "A Russki, huh?"

"Tibetan," I hurried to say. "And I'm a New Yorker, but by way of North Dakota."

"We're proud Ohioans!"

"Nice state," I said.

"The best!" the man boomed. The woman, attractive but tight-faced and heavily made-up, was frowning. At her husband, perhaps, or at Rinpoche's robe, or because of the mention of North Dakota. "The Buckeye state is the best state in the best country on earth!" her husband went on. He spoke very loudly and forcefully, as if he wanted to pre-empt any objection to the greatness of the place he called home.

"Good football teams," was the comment that came to mind, so that is what I said.

"OSU, Baby!" he yelled. *The* Ohio State University. Feeder school for half the frickin' NFL."

I nodded pleasantly, offered a smile, but it felt to me that, whenever he spoke, the light in the room changed slightly, as if he were casting a thin blanket over the sparkle.

Elsa carried out the dishes of pancakes. Real maple syrup, I noted. Butter, blueberries, and raspberries, ice water, coffee refills from a silver pitcher—all the bases covered. Rinpoche and I thanked her. She smiled and disappeared into the kitchen.

"What's with the getup, though?" the man asked. "Costume party or something, ha ha!"

Rinpoche, unflappable as ever, said, "I'm the monk."

"No shit! And you guys are what? To each other, I mean."

"Brothers-in-law," I said. "He married my sister."

"Ha!" The man stuffed a piece of pancake into his mouth, chewed twice, and washed it down with a gulp of the excellent coffee.

"I thought monks were celibate," the woman said. "We're Edie and Mike Revers, by the way. And you are?"

"Otto Ringling and Volya Rinpoche. Nice to meet you both."

"Strange names," she said.

"The wife has no tact," the man boomed, slicing off another piece of the stack in front of him. "Never had any."

"Who's talking," the wife said.

"We fight all the time," Mike barreled on. "I'm always right and, in the end, she always admits it. Spices up our sex life, ha!"

"Nice try," Edie said.

I did what I could to immerse myself in the food, sending a subtle message. The message was not received.

"You know, come to think of it, I like that you can get married," Mike said, pointing his fork at Rinpoche. "I hate the whole idea of giving up sex, though Edie here is lukewarm on the subject these days, right, Hon?"

"If my partner made it more enjoyable, maybe I'd be more into it."

"Oof," the man said, laughing, and then, "I mean, I agree with Jesus. *Carpe diem*, you know. Sex, food, drink, travel. You only live once. Grab what you can get, is my theorem on the subject."

"We think you live many time," Rinpoche said pleasantly.

"Like what?" Edie asked him. "A goat, an ant, a tree?"

"Yes."

"Makes no sense whatsoever," Mike said. "No sense. One life, one shot. *Carpe diem.*"

Rinpoche and I held to our silences, which, of course, only emboldened the good fellow. "Where's the proof, I'd like to know," he boomed. "For this reincarnation gobbledy-gook."

"Maybe how much compassion you have says how many lives you lived, is the proof. And I say 'we think', not 'we know'."

"Right, because you can't know."

I felt my patience leave me then, sand leaking from a torn pants pocket. Slowly at first, and then suddenly. "But *you* can know, I guess. I mean, you're a hundred per cent sure there's only one life."

"Absolutely. Utterly."

"We're sure," Edie added.

"Well, she agrees with me on that for one thing. There's a shocker."

For the second time, I tried to busy myself with the food. Rinpoche was doing the same. The strategy didn't work.

"There's no God, either," Edie spat. "If there was a loving God, how could he allow what's happening in Ukraine? In American politics."

"What your people, the Russkis are doing," Mike added, pointing his fork in Rinpoche's direction a second time. The fork had a bit of syrupy pancake on its tines, and the morsel of pancake dropped onto the tablecloth. Mike made two half-hearted efforts to pick it up again, smearing syrup everywhere, then surrendered and let it be.

"Honey, you're one, making a mess. And two, speaking very loud, which is what you always do when we meet new people."

"Sorry, you're right for once." Mike began to whisper. "Your demon Putin. You think a God would allow that?"

Edie elbowed him.

"I don't know," Rinpoche whispered back to him.

I laughed. I couldn't help myself. I was instantly sorry.

Mike shot me a vicious look. "*I don't know* is the easy way out."

"Maybe, *carpe diem* is the easy way out," I said, because by then all the sand had leaked out of my pocket, my little motorcar had raced past the polite-police checkpoint, the river had overflowed its bank. A variety of images came to mind. "And it wasn't Jesus who said that."

"If he even existed," Mike said. His large eyebrows were fluttering. He speared a piece of bacon and raised it to his mouth.

"Why you want the fight?" Rinpoche asked. "Why so angry now? Why so many people angry now?"

"Tired of the government telling me what to do, that's why, Mister Monk-who-has-sex. That I can't eat meat or white bread or Budweiser beer. That I can't have fun and enjoy my life, after all the decades of working. That I have to feel guilty about nine million things *other* people did three hundred frickin' years ago. That I have to get a shot, wear a mask, say or don't say certain words, hold certain views."

"We never said any of that," I said.

"I can see it just by looking at you. You said you're from New York."

"North Dakota, originally. And we just sat down and said hello, that's all. There are lots of different kinds of people in New York."

"We can see it in your faces, it's an attitude," Edie said. "A superiority. Nobody walks around in a robe like that who isn't trying to convert people."

"I give talks," Rinpoche admitted. "One more to go."

Edie smiled. "See?"

"What do you talk about?" Mike asked.

"Different things. The spirchal."

"See?" Edie said again. "I knew it. *Spiritual*, even when pronounced right, is a word I hate."

"Me, too," Rinpoche said, and for a brief moment he succeeded in quieting them.

"But you talk about it."

"You should come listen," Rinpoche said pleasantly. "Will be a good one, maybe, this last one."

"I won't waste my time," Mike said. "I know everything I need to know. I asked all the questions I needed to ask when I was about seventeen. And I answered them. You have as much fun as you can, then you die. Poof. Nothing."

"Could be," Rinpoche said. "Nobody know it."

"Somethings you just feel . . . if you have common sense."

At that juncture in our pleasant morning conversation, a woman came in alone and sat at the head of the table to my left. She was in her forties, I guessed, wearing a yellow and blue flowered dress, her hair pulled back into a short ponytail in the style Jeannie had favored. Wire-rimmed eyeglasses, slight build, a happy air. "Good morning, all!" she said cheerily. "What are we discussing?"

"Life after death," I said.

Edie and Mike let out identical guffaws. "Not hardly," Mike said, and we introduced ourselves.

The woman, who told us her name was Juniper, said to Elsa, "I'll have what they're having," and laughed a high-pitched staccato laugh I'd describe as 'merry'. And then, swinging her eyes around the table, "You mean what awaits us after we cross the lavender bridge?"

"Rainbow bridge, I thought it was," I said. My mood was becoming fouler and fouler as the minutes passed. The sand was gone, the little motorcar was racing, I was up to my neck in floodwater, angry as anyone, half-ashamed.

"I knew it!" Edie said. "There's the gay stuff."

"The rainbow had to come in somewhere," Mike agreed. "We knew that."

"*Raduga,* the Russian word," Rinpoche said.

"After crossing that bridge, whatever you call it, you enter the world of peace and love," Juniper went on, oblivious, apparently, to the various sciroccos of tension swirling across and around the beautiful table. "I lost my beloved partner, Hunter, just a month ago."

"*Partner*," Mike said, as if he might spit.

She smiled at him. "And I can sense them now in the realm above us. It eases my pain."

"We're glad," Edie said, "but first of all, doesn't 'they' mean two people or more? And there is no realm. It's a joke. A trick."

"Oh, I don't believe so," Juniper said happily. "Hunter's goodness and beauty will guide them into the most peaceful rooms of the mansion of the spirit. I'm sure of that."

"It's just a way of making yourself feel good," Mike said. "*Carpe diem, carpe diem.*"

Juniper reached out and put her hand lovingly on Mike's big forearm. He flinched. "Oh, see, there's another sign. Hunter used to say that all the time. *Carpe Diem.* Enjoy life, it means."

"It means 'seize the day', actually."

"He's the intellectual in the bunch," Edie said, lifting her chin in my direction.

Juniper kept smiling—at Mike, at Edie, at me, at Rinpoche, at Elsa when she carried in another serving of pancakes. Juniper smiled at the pancakes, asked if there might possibly be herbal tea. "And you're a Tibetan Buddhist monk, a Rinpoche, right?" she said.

"Yes."

"That's just so great!"

The pancakes were delicious, the coffee strong, the light coming in through the room's many windows was a pleasant light.

I heard footsteps on the floor behind me and felt someone

entering the room through the doorway there. "Diversity," Mike muttered. Edie's lips twitched. She elbowed him so hard in the side that he said, "Ouch, honey," and then, "Hi!'

The "Hi" was aimed at a large man with wire-framed eye-glasses who took the seat at the other end of the table, to my right, opposite Juniper. "George Harrelson," he said.

"A Beatle!" Mike boomed.

No one laughed.

We introduced ourselves. George ordered the pancakes. "What a nice group!" he said. "Where you all from?"

Juniper, it turned out, hailed from New Mexico and was making a tour of the eastern seaboard.

"Wow!" George said, "Ohio, North Dakota, New York, Siberia, New Mexico. South Carolina, for me. God has brought us together on this beautiful morning."

"Oh, boy," Mike said.

George didn't seem to hear. When his food was served, he sat quietly, head bowed, hands folded in front of his forehead, and said a brief prayer.

Mike harrumphed. "Pancakes gettin' cold."

"But we must thank the Good Lord first," George said. He and Juniper could hardly have been more different, physically: she was white and small, he black and large—but they seemed cut from the same cloth of temperament: grateful, upbeat, slow to anger. Perhaps partly oblivious.

"Let's not talk about God anymore, can we?" Edie said. "It just causes trouble."

"As you wish," George said. "I'm a preacher, though, so it's a natural subject for me."

"Right, well, I used to be a hairdresser, but I don't talk about hair all the time."

George laughed, unoffended. Juniper, perhaps finally sensing the mood, had started humming while she ate. Rinpoche was very carefully cleaning the last bit of blueberry from his syrupy plate.

"Good pancakes," I said. "I was an editor of food books."

"And I'm a medium," Juniper said. "I contact those in the other realms."

"Talk to your Hunter lately?" Mike asked.

The smile slipped from Juniper's face like snow from a roof on a sunny February morning. She shook her head.

"Leave her the Christ alone, will you, Mike," Edie said, before I could say something similar.

"It's often true that we can't reach our closest loved ones until they've inhabited the other realms for a certain period of earthly time."

"I'm sure he's fine in heaven and waiting for you to join him," George said.

"*They* are," Edie said caustically.

Juniper seemed as if she might cry. Elsa brought the herbal tea.

I was finished with my food, and still coated—despite the *tonglen* and the talk with Rinp—in disappointment from the visit with Anthony. I could actually *feel* it. I was angry at Edie and Mike and ashamed of being angry. I looked at Rinpoche, hoping we could decide, just with eye contact, that the time had come to leave. But it was not to be.

"I used to ride the horses with my father when I was a boy," Rinpoche said, out of nowhere.

"Oh, I *adore* riding!" Juniper said.

"Grew up on a horse farm," George put in.

"Well, you and me both," Mike said. "That's how Edie and me met, at an event. She was a beautiful rider."

"The horses can be bodhisattvas," Rinpoche said, and four

quizzical expressions greeted the remark. I wondered whether I should try to explain. "Dogs, too," he said.

"We just lost ours," Edie said. "Wolfgang. Longhaired German Shepherd. Best dog ever created."

"Mine died, too!" Juniper and George exclaimed at the same moment.

"And I lost my beloved Jasper some years ago," I put in hopefully. "No love like that."

"Damn right about that."

"You feed them, take them out for a walk, give them a place to sleep, and they love you like no human being ever could."

"Why?" Rinpoche asked.

"Why what?"

"Why dogs and horses can love you so much?"

"What a good question!" Juniper exclaimed.

"Because they're short on opinions," George suggested.

"And they don't care what you look like!" Edie put in. "How your hair looks, your face, your nails."

"Nothing wrong with looking good," Mike said.

"They see something beyond the surfaces," I heard myself say.

"Just as Christ does," George added.

Juniper made a small jump, lifting herself an inch out of her chair. "That's beautiful! That's why I was brought here this morning, to hear you say that, Reverend! Thank you!"

"We can't live like dogs and horses," Mike grumbled.

A moment of silence descended upon the table. Elsa came and removed the plates of those who had finished. "More coffee?" she asked.

There were no takers.

"Do you have the dog?" Rinpoche asked Elsa.

Her face lit up. "I do! How did you know?"

"I can see it on you."

She looked down at her shirt as if there might be some stray hairs there.

"He means he can see it in you," I said.

"Oh, well yes. Buddy. We rescued him."

"No, he rescued you!" Juniper said.

"It's too much, really. This is too much. Let's go hon."

Mike and Edie stood up. Elsa looked confused. "It was nice meeting all of you," Edie said, sarcastically, but by then her husband was out the door.

"God bless!" George called.

"Blessings!" Juniper added.

"Christ Almighty!" I heard Mike say from the other room. "Let's go, will you?"

There was another short patch of silence, and then Juniper noted, happily, "They're from Ohio."

"You know," George was looking at Rinpoche, "I think I'm going to get a sermon out of this, out of your question. Dogs and horses. What was that word you used?"

"Bodhisattva," I said, answering for Rinpoche. "In Buddhism it's a being who's reincarnated for the benefit of others."

"Like Christ Jesus."

"Exactly."

"It's just so beautiful," Juniper said.

"Yes."

All through the meal and the tumultuous conversation, I'd been trying to get a sense of Rinpoche's take on it all. He was sitting quietly now, hands in his lap, prayer beads going, on his face the usual serene expression. "Ready to hit the road, Rinp?" I asked, but he seemed tuned to another frequency.

He just looked at me, then at George. "What church you work inside?"

"Bethel A.M.E. in Georgetown, South Carolina. The first black church in the state, 1863. I'm on a little two-day vacation, visiting some cousins up here. I'll be back there on Sunday, though. Would you like to talk there, Sir? We often have guest preachers."

"Thank you, but I just listen maybe. We going that way, Otto?"

"We could."

"Then I want to. Any people can come?"

"We welcome everyone."

"Then we see you," Rinpoche said. He stood up and bowed to George and Juniper, bowed to and thanked Elsa. On our way out, through the magnificent dining room with its oriental carpet and elaborate chandelier, he put his arm around my shoulder and said, "Give the woman some lot of money for the tip, Otto. Did you see her spirit?"

"She seemed nice. Excellent service."

"Big spirit," he said. At the desk I asked for an envelope, wrote ELSA on it, put in three hundreds, sealed it, and left it with the kind woman there.

Twenty-Six

Just as we finished loading our bags into the truck and were about to leave the parking lot of the Morehead Inn, literally just after I'd taken my place in the passenger seat, closed the door, and was reaching for the seat belt, I spotted Edie sitting alone and weeping on a metal bench at the far edge of the courtyard. Rinpoche was already turning toward the exit, and I had to crane my neck over my right shoulder to keep looking at her. Definitely Edie, definitely weeping. For one second, I thought of asking Rinpoche to stop. I'd get out, hustle over to the bench, ask what was wrong, offer a few words of comfort. It was just an impulse, a reflex, a peace offering, something to make up for my nasty mood at the breakfast table. But, almost as soon as the thought appeared, I set it aside. As I engaged Google Maps and turned up the volume on my phone so Rinp could hear, and as we worked our way very, very slowly out of the quiet neighborhood and toward the highway, I wondered if it was the breakfast conversation that had upset her, or if it was being reminded of the loss of her favorite dog, or the end of her days as a competitive equestrienne. Or if her sorrow had its roots in being married to Mike, enduring and trying to parry his constant barrage of upsetting comments, or being paired in spirit with someone who felt compelled to spout opinions, constantly, and who took of-

207

fense at everything from meeting a New Yorker to hearing the word 'rainbow.'

I remembered Reverend George saying that dogs and horses could love so purely, "because they're short on opinions," and it occurred to me that, battered by opinions as she must be, day after day, sensitized to every word and inference, and expressing strong opinions herself, Edie weeping on the bench was the perfect symbol for America in our divisive era. Not so long ago, our opinions had been relegated to dinner tables, barrooms, and letters to the local newspaper (and even then they'd been the cause of minor societal disruption—two local farmers no longer speaking to one another outside our church in the Reagan years, for one North Dakota example). Now we were positively drowning in opinions, most of them expressed at top volume. A five-minute scroll through social media seemed to bring out the wannabe tough guy in everyone. The TV news wasn't news anymore, or not only news; it was ribboned with opinion, sometimes striped with ridicule and mockery. Instead of solving our problems, this flood of opinion had merely brought us millions of people like Mike, desperate to be heard, to be right, not to be 'forced' to do anything they didn't want to do.

In my opinion, anyway.

Musing along these lines, I saw, too, what a master stroke it had been for Rinpoche to take a conversation that could have led to shouting matches, or worse, and turn it in the direction of a moment of commonality.

"Rinp," I said, when we were safely on Route 74 and rolling along in the slow lane, "what made you start talking about horses?"

"I like them wery much, the horses."

I hummed a skeptical response, because I knew by then

that his mysterious sixth sense had been at work, that he'd been traveling at speeds no one else at that table could quite match, that, instead of getting up and walking away, he'd deftly encouraged the rest of us to step free of our morass of disagreement and onto common ground.

I found myself wondering if there was any chance, any chance at all, that my brother-in-law might one day run for public office.

As we moved eastward through south-central North Carolina, the rain eased and finally stopped. The landscape there was peaceful, if not particularly interesting, fields and low hills, trees not trusting the warmth enough to reach more than the tips of their first tender shoots into the air. I couldn't keep my thoughts from returning to Anthony. Another symbol of modern America, perhaps, since he'd decided there was no such thing as 'enough.' I was thinking about a nation of such incredible wealth, and yet one where mass shootings were more and more common, where the rates of suicide, depression, and addiction were, by any historical standard, astronomical. Could it be that too many of us—myself included—had made a wrong turn at some point? Had we learned to worship the wrong kind of god, the god of infinitely increasing convenience and infinitely refined pleasures? And were we blinded, because of that worship, by a collective hypnosis, a mantra of *more, more, more?*

In the past, in the glory days of my career advancement, Manhattan luncheons, and family travel, I'd thought of my sister's humble life in the humble city of Paterson, New Jersey, as being an example of failure, a dead-end street I wanted my children to avoid. She had nothing, went nowhere, drove around in a dented, fifteen-year-old Pontiac, and ate peanut butter sandwiches for lunch on her rickety back deck. Although I never said anything like this to her directly, I told myself she'd thrown away so much potential, wasted her intelligence, buried her vibrant personality in the compost pile of her backyard garden.

How many years had it taken me to look beyond the typical definition of success and appreciate her wisdom, her focus on loving and giving, her gift of optimism and hope, even in the hardest times!

We'd gone only an hour or so when Rinpoche swerved suddenly to the right. I'd been lost in thought, as the expression goes, and was about to reach for the steering wheel and keep us from crashing, when I saw that he'd turned—too abruptly— into the parking lot of a small wooden building with a sign for *Real Southern Bar-B-Que* out front. He parked and said, "You hungry?"

"No, for once. Are you?"

"Just for the tea with ice. Sweet kind."

"Let's go in."

We stepped out of the truck and crunched in tandem across the gravel lot.

Inside, the place was Spartan, half of it filled with knick-knacks for sale on four wooden tables, and half with the restaurant, such as it was. On the plank walls hung a collection of old-fashioned signs and advertisements—Moxie, Chesterfields, cartoons from *Leave it to Beaver*—as if the owners longed for the good ol' days when life was simple, and you could have a smoke without feeling guilty. Behind the narrow counter stood a young fellow so clean-cut he might have stepped off the Liberty U. campus between classes, and through a doorway to one side of him I caught a glimpse of a young woman, possibly his sister, working at a stove. Rinp took a seat at one of the tables.

I decided at the last second that I was hungry after all, ordered the brisket sandwich, asked to have it cut in half, and carried large cups of sweet iced tea over to my traveling companion.

It may sometimes seem that, in describing these road trips with my brother-in-law, I engage in certain fabrications in order to enhance the story. I do not. For various reasons, in some cases—as in this one—I will omit the name of a restaurant or person, but I don't make up what we see along the routes we travel, and I don't lie about the food we eat. I say this because, on that cloudy North Carolina afternoon, with my feelings about the visit to Anthony rising and falling, splashing and receding like a seaweed-choked tide along the sandy shores of my old brain, I saw, on a half-wall against which our table stood, a few inches from my shoulder, a framed drawing of the cars of a nineteenth-century train, accompanied by these words: *"Train up a child in the way he should go." Proverbs 23:6.*

While we waited for our sandwich, I Googled the quote to see if it was accurate. It was. The rest of the injunction went like this: "And when he is old, he will not depart from it."

I must have made some noise, a sigh, a grunt, a quiet wail, because when I looked up from my telephone, Rinpoche had his eyes fixed on me in a way I recognized.

"What goin' on, Otto?" he asked.

I shook my head at first, looked away, looked back, "Still thinking about Anthony, that's all."

Rinpoche nodded and was about to say something when we were summoned to collect our meal. The sandwich, it turned out, came with a side of barbecued beans. I set the plate between us, took up my half, and had a bite. The brisket tasted like it had been sitting on the counter since lunch the week before and had been hastily heated up.

Rinpoche was still eyeing me.

"I know, I know," I said, once I'd managed to swallow. "I should let it go. He was busy, he's young. I know."

"You have the big job comin' up now," Rinpoche said, before spooning some beans into his mouth. A quick wash of displeasure crossed his face. "You got to get your mind ready for it."

"I thought I was done with the big jobs. Kids, house, retirement. I thought the big jobs were behind me."

He shook his head, took a smaller taste. "In front from you now, Otto."

"Don't tell me I'm going to father and raise another child."

"Other kind of big job."

"Going to start a company that makes semi-conductors? Going to plant a crop of spring wheat?"

More headshaking.

"Going to attend hairdressing school and open up a little unisex shop in Bismarck?"

"No, Siree," he said, an expression I'd never heard from him.

"You got that from Les Ingler, that 'No, Siree.'"

A huge smile. "Yep."

"When is this big job coming my way?"

"Soon," he said. "Real big one! Maybe in your life, the biggest!" And then, whispering, "Beans not that good!"

I leaned in closer and whispered, "Brisket not that good!"

"We take 'em for make-out," he said.

"*Take* out, not make-out. That's a different pleasure." But before I could say anything else he was at the counter, asking for a "not too big box for the make-out."

It took a few seconds for the clean-cut lad to understand what was being asked of him. We sat with the take-out box while we finished our tea—which tasted fine; it's hard to spoil sweet tea—and then we carried our lunch out of the establishment. En route to the pickup, we passed a large trash barrel. Rinpoche stopped beside it and turned his eyes to me again. "Put your bad thoughts now in here," he said, opening the takeout container and holding it over the barrel.

"What do you mean?"

"The bad thoughts about Anthony. You put them in here with the bad food now."

I tried.

He studied me for a moment, nodded, and, with a comical flourish, dropped the box into the barrel.

Twenty-Seven

"I hate to waste food like that," I said, as we headed east again on the two-lane highway, Rinpoche still behind the wheel. "I shouldn't have ordered it in the first place. Sorry."

"Tasted like shit," Rinp said.

"You got that expression from Les, too, right? You know it's not something you should say in public."

"You not public."

"Right. And I agree with the one-star review. A shame, because North Carolina's famous for its barbeque."

Rinpoche shrugged, glanced in the rear view, leaned another inch forward in his seat.

Seese had told me once that her husband sometimes went a full week without eating, subsisting only on water for all that time. It had worried her at first, she said, but now she was used to it. I remembered reading similarly unusual accounts of Christian saints (some aspiring young author had offered a book on that subject to the publishing house where I worked), and also apparently accurate stories of yogis who could perform a headstand with their noses and mouth buried in sand, and remain like that overnight, not breathing. I wondered sometimes if Rinpoche had been taught those techniques, or similar ones, and could control his appetite to a degree that seemed dangerous to me. I'd seen him in a yoga class, moving into and out of the poses effortlessly. I'd seen him lift heavy objects without hurting his back. I'd seen him pin Anthony to the ground in a few seconds during their friendly wrestling matches, when Anthony had been playing college football. Many times, I'd asked Rinp about his upbringing and training, but other than saying his father was a great teacher and had been imprisoned in Siberia for his religious activity, and other than answering my questions about the mysterious 'root-energy' Tai Chi or whatever it was, Rinpoche hadn't been very forthcoming about his past.

So I tried a different approach. "Was your mother a good cook?"

"The best, Otto."

"What did you grow up eating? When you were a kid in Skovorodino."

"Tibetan food," he said. "From the yak. The milk, the meat, some butter. Grains, too. I don't know the name for them in English."

"What's the word for yak?"

"*Yak*. Same word."

"No vegetables?"

"Not too many. How you say? The firms, when the snow went away."

"Ferns, you mean."

"Yes."

"No fruit?"

"The apples."

"How come you're so healthy then, with that kind of a diet?"

"Mind had a good diet."

"No TV, right? No computer games? No worries about car repairs and unmown lawns?"

"You know it, man," he said. Another Les-ism.

"You'll live to be a hundred and twenty," I said, but he was focused on the road and didn't respond.

Near the city of Hamlet, we pulled off the highway to fill up with gas and take another 'breathing.' We strolled along the small, not-unattractive downtown, which was enlivened by a massive train depot with a conical red roof. I took a photo of the building—two stories, scores of windows, the remarkable roof—and sent it to Natasha, adding a note that things were going well, we were enjoying the trip, and asking about her life. "Anthony had your beautiful photos on his office wall," I wrote. "I think I'll be back on the farm pretty soon. Miss and love you."

Phone still in hand (Rinpoche's in his luggage), I figured Seese would want to talk to her husband, so I dialed the farm and handed Rinp the phone. We sat side-by-side on a bench and I could hear my sister's sunny "Hello!"

"Good sweetheart!" Rinpoche greeted her, "now me and your good brother are sitting on the bench and watching the train tracks!"

He switched the phone to his other ear, holding it with thumb and middle finger as he liked to do, and from that point I could hear only one side of the conversation. "Yes, wery good! Pancakes with the blue berries, and people who liked horses!" "Yes!" "We met a man wanted me to preach." "No." A shrug of his big shoulders. "It's his church, my good wife. He should be the preaching, not me this time." A pause. "In the south of Carolina. An Amy church." Another pause. "Amy." "I don't think so." He took the phone from his ear and turned to me. "How they call the man's church, Otto?"

"A . . . M . . . E.," I said, loud enough for my sister to hear. "African Methodist Episcopal."

"You heard of?" Rinpoche chuckled. "All these years and still can't talk so good." "Yes, I know." He turned to me again. "In what city is the church, Otto."

"Georgetown, South Carolina."

"You heard? Yes, he loves you back. Yes. Can we go near there? Can you find us the place?" A pause, a nod or two. "You talkin' to him soon? He looked so good! Handsome, but didn't want to wessle!" He waved a hand, as if to assure me the wrestling idea had been a joke. "Okay, good. Love for you too, also, and for our beautiful daughter that I am missing, and for Natasha my good nieces." "Yes." "All right, not too bad, don't worry, okay?" "Good. Love you, my wife, bye."

Rinpoche looked at the screen and used his index finger to punch the red circle and end the call. His face was split by the widest smile I'd seen on the whole trip. He sighed and looked up at the clouded sky as if giving thanks.

"Everything good at home?" I asked.

He turned his head, and the smile was like a light being shone on me, a light of the purest happiness, brightening the day. "Not couldn't be better," he said.

Twenty-Eight

As we strolled back toward the parked truck, I happened to see, beyond a picnic bench set in a patch of greenery twenty yards diagonally in front of us, a woman walking out of the trees. She was a large woman, in her thirties or perhaps early forties, and what caught my eye at first was the way she was rearranging her long, colorful skirt. It took me two more seconds to realize that she'd just been using the trees as her bathroom, and that the green plastic garbage bag on the picnic table belonged to her. She fluffed and straightened her skirt for another few steps, then sat at the table, and lay her head down on bare, fleshy forearms. The skin of her arms was covered with raw spots, as if she'd been bitten by a horde of mosquitoes. I admit here that I've always made a point of not giving money to people like that woman—the ones who stand on street corners with handwritten cardboard signs, or sit slumped against the fronts of buildings on a Manhattan sidewalk, surrounded by their earthly belongings. Occasionally I made an exception—if the person was blind, missing a leg, or in a wheelchair; on cold days I'd buy a cup of coffee for one of them, or hand over, at a stoplight, an apple or a candy bar I happened to have in the front seat. But I worried that giving money to those poor souls begging on street corners would only further the addiction that had likely sent them to the streets in the first place, that my cash would go to buy a pint of cheap wine, or a dose of heroin. Something about the woman at the picnic table cut through that assumption, or reservation, or habit. I veered away from Rinpoche and walked over to her.

"Excuse me," I said, and she lifted her face as if expecting to be told to go sleep someplace else. I peeled off some bills from the wad in my pocket, folded them and held them out. "Please get yourself something to eat," I said. She took the bills, and then, without a word, reached out her other hand, palm-down. I took her hand, held it for a few seconds, then turned and walked back across the ragged strip of grass. For once, I wasn't conflicted or guilty or unsure. For once, thanks to those few seconds of physical contact, things seemed very simple.

To my surprise then, I saw that Rinpoche was getting up off the ground and brushing dirt from the front of his robe. "You fell, Rinp?"

He was chuckling. "The earth pulling at me already," he said.

"You okay?"

"A little old, Otto, that's all."

It was a first: I'd never seen him trip or fall. I'd never heard him refer to himself as old. I watched him all the way back to the truck, but he seemed fine.

Rinp said he wanted to keep driving, and I was more or less happy to let him do so. From what I'd gathered from his half of the conversation with Seese, it sounded like we were heading for Georgetown, South Carolina, so I asked him not to start the truck for a minute, and checked the map on my phone, trying to find a direct route. There wasn't a direct route. "Let's just stay on 74 and wait for Seese to get us the address of the hotel," I said.

Rinp shrugged, smiled, unworried as ever, and we set off.

Near the city of Lumberton, we somehow lost our grip on Route 74, or Route 74 somehow lost its grip on us, and we ended up on a much smaller road, 211, that sliced through the hamlets of Butters and Bladenboro. And then, in Delco, we stumbled upon I-74 again. I felt my phone buzz, and, thinking it was Seese with the name of our hotel, I switched from the map and saw this text, all in lower case:

> sorry, pop. i was an ass not to have breakfast
> with you guys. aunt seese just called. she said Rinp
> told her you're heading for georgetown, s.c. If you're near
> wilmington now, if you went that way, have lunch at my
> favorite mexican place, the island grill. I just rented a
> house for you guys on the beach in litchfield in south
> carolina, not far off route 17. a beautiful beach and one
> of my favorite places on earth. my secretary is sending the
> address. you'll be pretty close to georgetown. love you both
> more than I can ever say. your stupid son. anth.

I held the phone with both hands and read the message three times, then looked out the side window and wiped the tops of both cheeks dry, remembering, hoping, glad I hadn't said what I'd been thinking of saying.

"Good news?" Rinpoche asked, but I could manage only a nod and an indecipherable syllable

The Island Grill was hidden away in a strip mall in an otherwise residential section on the fringes of Wilmington. By the time we walked through the door, it was two p.m., and I was seriously hungry. At first glance, the eatery didn't strike me as particularly promising: you grabbed a tray and ordered your meal at the start of a cafeteria line. I stood there perusing the overhead menu, wrestling with a weird flashback to the dining hall at UND, where, in those fine old days before salad bars and gluten-free options, you'd be presented—after a long, tiring hockey practice, for example—with chipped beef on toast, Salisbury steak, chicken a la king, or mashed potatoes from a mix. It occurred to me that my career editing food books might have begun on one of those evenings, gazing down the line at a dish of rubbery string beans.

I ordered a chicken burrito and said, when asked, "Put everything on it, everything you have."

"Everything, really?"

"Yes."

Rinp went with a vegetarian taco. He paid from the wad he carried in one of the deep and mysterious pockets of his robe (I should note here that he always carried a spare robe in his leather satchel, and, every two days or so, either washed by hand the one he'd been wearing, or used the hotel laundry, if one was available). We were each given a paper bag of tortilla chips and went over to a glass-hooded, self-serve area and filled small plastic cups with various salsas. After we'd found a table, I went back and poured sweet tea into tall cups, and we began the refueling.

"Doesn't taste like shit," Rinpoche said, perhaps a bit loudly. A table of college students glanced over.

"A-plus in my book. Anthony knows his food."

A grunt, a smile, a sip of tea. One of my favorite Don Henley songs was playing on the speakers.

"And he said he rented us a house on the beach. Litchfield is the name of the place. Do you have a talk near there?"

"Could be. But I want to go to the church first. Sunday is tomorrow and I liked wery much the man from breakfast."

"Okay. It's an A.M.E church, though, as I said when you were talking to Seese. African Methodist Episcopal. We'll probably be the only not-black people in the congregation."

My brown-skinned brother-in-law gave me a quizzical look then, squinting his eyes and pursing his lips. Not criticizing, exactly, but puzzled that I'd say such a thing. 'What difference does that make?' the look said, and so I felt compelled to add, "I just hope we're welcome, that's all. Two years ago a white man prayed with parishioners at an A.M.E church pretty close to the one you want to go to, and then, when he'd finished praying, he took out a gun and killed seven people."

Rinpoche blinked. "The man at breakfast—"

"George."

"Yes, George invited us."

"Right, sorry. It was a stupid thing to say. George invited us, so we're welcome there. We'll go. No problem. Sorry."

The food was, in fact, top-shelf, perfect, delicious. I went back for another helping of chips and filled the small plastic cups with a spicier salsa this time. Rinpoche and I sat there for a long while, dipping and crunching and sipping, letting, in my case at least, the fullness of the moment return. From the time we'd left the upsetting breakfast conversation at the Morehead Inn, I'd been thinking about Anthony, worrying, judging, silently complaining, feeling that I'd failed, or that he'd failed, or that both of us had failed. His text and apology, his tone and generosity, had washed all that toxicity out of me and let me sink back into the warm fatherly love I'd always felt for him. I could see, again, the way the mind's penchant for NO could pollute that love. How strong opinions could pollute it. *NO you shouldn't act this way. You should have breakfast with us. You should make time. You should.* . . . I could see how hard it was, how important it was, to keep the fingers of judgment away from the lives of people you loved, so you wouldn't turn into a Mike in your old age. As well as I knew my own son, I could never really know the demons he wrestled with, the urges and insecurities, the fears and dreams, the intricacies of the karmic burden he carried. If my job had once been to love and guide him, it was now mostly just the former part of that.

And so, happy again, relieved, at peace, I proceeded to eat too much in celebration.

Twenty-Nine

Once Chantelle sent me the details on the house rental, I realized that Anthony had paid for the rental to start the next day, Sunday, and that we had to find a place to spend Saturday night. So, instead of staying in North Carolina, as I thought we might, Rinp and I decided to drive south from Wilmington on Route 17. It wasn't long until we passed into South Carolina, and then, it seemed, we'd entered the Enchanted Kingdom of Golf. Everywhere we looked there were golf communities, golf courses, or signs for golf communities and golf courses. Shops in roadside strip malls advertising golf clubs and golf shoes and golf shirts. Greens and sand traps separated from the highway by a single row of palm trees. Men in colorful caps, driving squat little carts, their clubs strapped on behind. I thought I could smell cigar smoke. Rinpoche, I knew, had played a few rounds with Anthony when we were in North Dakota, years earlier, and, at one of the seven hundred and twenty-five stoplights Route 17, I glanced over to get his reaction. He seemed to be asleep.

My dad hadn't played golf—I don't know many farmers who have time for it—and, though about a quarter of our friends in Bronxville were addicted to the game and held memberships at elite gathering spots like Siwanoy, Brae Burn, or Westchester Country Club, I'd never really been tempted. Before our children were born, Jeannie and I tried the sport a

224

couple of times on various vacation trips, and it had seemed to both of us the most difficult and frustrating activity ever invented. The televised PGA tournaments made it look easy, but, though we were reasonably athletic, we hit the ball sideways into the trees, or along the ground straight into water holes, or we missed the little white demon entirely, straining a wrist or shoulder in the process, and looked around to see if the damage we seemed to have done to the course warranted expulsion.

As Rinpoche and I approached Myrtle Beach, the situation worsened. More and more golf. I wondered if we'd be stopped by the South Carolina State Police; the officer would check for golf clubs in the back of the pickup, and, discovering that we didn't play, would levy a hefty fine that would go toward the cost of watering and grooming the fields of frustration we passed.

Dollar Tree, a flea market, yard sales, trailer parks, chain restaurants, malls, houses on stilts, churches, a Ukrainian flag on a pole in front of a storage facility, more golf courses, and stoplight after stoplight until, at last, we passed out of the commercial area and onto the non-business Route 17. Two lanes with Spanish moss hanging from ancient live oaks by the sides of the road, a small makeshift hut with a woman weaving reed baskets, her work displayed on hooks around her. Then the Brookgreen Botanical Gardens and, at last, the entrance to our hotel.

"We fast rest of today," Rinpoche said, and I felt a cold shiver go through me. I'd had a difficult twenty-four hours, a stretch of roller-coaster emotions, and I'd been imagining dinner that evening as a kind of salve. Seafood or barbecue, more of the sweet tea. A hush puppy or three for dessert.

But no. We were fasting again.

Our third-floor room was pleasant enough. Two queen

beds, clean bath, desk, couch, a soft chair—what else could a fasting person ask for? "Long meditation now," Rinpoche said when we'd washed up and rested from the road. He pulled two pillows from the couch and arranged himself on the floor, cross-legged. I sat in one of the chairs, closed my eyes, relaxed my body, and began a familiar dance with my restless mind. It jumped from thought to thought, worry to plan to memory to idle speculation. My eyes flickered beneath the lids, seeking, seeking. For a time, without intending to, I imagined myself playing golf, signing up for a course in North Dakota and becoming adept at the game, making friends, talking bogeys and three-putts, seeing if Natasha might be interested. I caught myself and brought my mind back. It flipped to Rein's, to Anthony's kindness, to wondering what Seese would do next— surprise us with another scheduled talk, this one at a mosque or synagogue? Make hotel arrangements in the Florida panhandle? Tell us we absolutely had to go to New Orleans so Rinpoche could hear some jazz or blues? I wondered what our reception would be like next day at the A.M.E. I wondered how long Rinpoche would keep us sitting there. I felt a pang of hunger, a twinge in my lower back.

And then, very gradually, because I didn't try to resist or control it, and since I wasn't appalled or excited by any of it, all that mental activity began to settle. There were thoughts, still— would Rinp wake up with sore knees from his fall? Was it too early to look into an oil change for his new truck? Might it be possible to swim in front of the beach house Anthony had rented? Had I brought a bathing suit? Could I buy one at this time of year? Would Anthony surprise us with a visit?—but those thoughts seemed less *sticky* somehow, rising into view for a moment, then slipping away. I felt a familiar feeling of *sinking down*—that's the only way to describe it—below the run of interior busyness. Thoughts, images, memories, and plans appeared, but now, instead of coming in a fast stream that carried me off, they floated in like bubbles blown from a child's toy. Drifted into view, popped, and went away. For seconds at a time, there was nothing at all, just a presence, but it wasn't a bland presence; it had a tinge of joy to it, a calm pleasure, an inkling of some non-human dimension. Then another run of thoughts: Mike, Edie, anger, horses. Then *poof!* A longer stretch of quiet. Some musing like this for a while: *What if we turned out not to be welcome at the church, not welcome at all? What if Reverend Harrelson's offer had been a simple act of politeness, an invitation he never expected to be taken seriously?* Then quiet again. A minor-league version of what the Catholics called *quies.* No time passing.

Rinpoche coughed and stirred. I resisted an urge to look at my watch to see how long I'd managed to sit still. What difference did it make? It wasn't a competition. It wouldn't be recorded in some divine journal: Otto Ringling, one hour and so many minutes, bravo!

We lay down in our separate beds and I turned on the television. And what did I find on the screen?

Golf.

Thirty

In the morning, I awoke early, empty-bellied but more or less at peace. I'd had another disturbing dream—which accounts for the 'more or less'—with vague images of faces spinning in a silent whirl and a moonlit beach scene, and I was wrestling with it, reaching for the lost parts, trying to make sense of it as I showered and shaved. Rinpoche wasn't in the room. I dressed in the best clothes I'd brought with me and went downstairs, expecting to find him in the breakfast area with a Styrofoam plate of biscuits and eggs, with those wasteful little non-biodegradable packets of jelly and butter and a cup of dreary coffee. He wasn't there. Instead of taking plastic utensils and plate—I would have felt guilty, eating without him—I walked outside and found him seated on a concrete bench near the entrance, gazing peacefully at a sparrow pecking in the dirt nearby. For a moment, I just watched him, and for that moment I had the strange sense—one in a series of such impressions going back over several years—that he and the sparrow were made of the same *stuff*. I don't know how else to explain it. The sparrow was moving, Rinpoche was still. Small and large, bird and human, obviously. But I felt I could see, or sense, some connection between them, the essential link of life, the godly atoms in both bodies. And then Rinpoche turned his head and saw me and smiled.

"The coffee tasted like shit," he said, a bit too loudly. "The orange kind."

"Decaf."

"And the milk was inside small small cups. One drink, I had."

"Want to go out for breakfast?"

He shook his head. I felt the familiar chill go up my arms and guessed what he was about to say. "Lunch we can eat after the church, okay?"

"Sure, fine," I said, but there was a twist in my belly, and in my thoughts a smaller version of that same loud NO!

I wanted to eat.

We went upstairs and collected our things. Thinking of Alinda and her beautiful children back in Greater Boston, I left the largest tip yet for the woman who would clean our room, we checked out, and, Rinp behind the wheel again, headed south toward the city of Georgetown.

The night before, because watching the professional golfers had made me feel clumsy, and because there was no dinner on our schedule, I'd spent a little time online, reading about Georgetown. Its history seemed sad to me, a sad American tale, the Natives chased away, the economy booming because of indigo and then rice plantations, both dependent on slave labor for their survival. Brookgreen, the botanical gardens we'd passed on the drive south, turned out to have been the main plantation of Joshua John Ward who, at one time, had been the largest slave owner in the United States. With the Civil War and the abolition of slavery, the rice plantations failed, and the area became an important producer of lumber. At one point after World War II, Georgetown was home to the largest paper mill in the world, and then huge steel and chemical plants. It made me think of Shelsa and her incendiary comments on capitalism, made me want to sit down and discuss those comments with her. It seemed clear to me that no system humanity had ever devised was better at producing the goods a population needed—and some it didn't need. Capitalism enhanced the development of everything from medicines to transportation, and lifted billions of people out of subsistence farming and into a level of luxury that would have been completely unimaginable before the creation of the interlocking gears of capital and markets.

At the same time—and I guessed this must have been the heart of her criticism—the immeasurable wealth and the imponderable availability of foodstuffs and goods was like a treasure chest holding a million pounds of diamonds, that was carried here and there on the backs of the working poor. The books my former employer sold, a product that had given me and my family a lifestyle 99% of the people on earth would envy, had come, not only from the brains and experiences of their authors and the skill of editors, publicists, agents, but from the paper mills where workers sweated and breathed poison and lived for a day or two of rest at the end of the week, and a week or two of relaxation in any given year. The mansions of Charleston and the elegant gardens of Brookgreen had been paid for with the sweat and blood of slaves, a currency of pure torture.

On the way to the A.M.E. church, we took a wrong turn and ended up driving past Georgetown's steel mill, a dark, hulking mass in the bowels of which people had toiled for generations. Could we have been riding in the fine silver pickup without millions of adulthoods being spent in such places? Rinpoche was sure that we lived many, many lives, some rich and some poor, some as the plantation owner, some as the slave, and so perhaps there was, ultimately, a form of justice.

But I supposed Shelsa was agitating for more justice *now,* more of a sense of appreciation for the women who cleaned hotel toilets and the men who spent their days in the bellies of enormous factories. In a sense, the whole idea of giving money away, as I was trying to do in some reasonable fashion, was a minuscule attempt to admit that I had *enough*—the word not spoken in Anthony's office. And that others did not.

We found the Bethel African Methodist Episcopal church on a side street lined with trees and modest houses, and angle-parked not far away. The building was an imposing, if somewhat worn, redbrick structure, with a pair of fortress-like towers out front, and the narrow stained glass windows that reminded me of St. John's Lutheran, where our family had worshipped in Dickinson.

Covid, it seemed, had hit the congregation as hard in the past two years as Hurricane Hugo had hit the town three decades earlier. We were required to wear masks, to undergo a temperature check at the door, to sign a piece of paper saying we weren't suffering from any of the usual symptoms. Only then were we allowed into the nave. Intricate tin roof, the pipes of a large organ behind the altar, a plain cross there, a choir in gowns. And our friend George Harrelson from The Morehead Inn sitting in a chair awaiting the start of services. He nodded to us and offered a small smile. Rinpoche and I took seats in the rear pew and were handed a sort of program by a beautifully dressed elderly black woman wearing a bright pink hat. There were fewer than a hundred people in attendance, most pews mostly empty, but I could see a camera on a tripod facing the altar and assumed the service was being broadcast to those who preferred to worship in the safety of their home.

I wish I could have recorded the service. I thought of doing so, in fact, but decided it would be disrespectful, and took careful mental notes instead. Reverend George V. Harrelson opened with a prayer that included another nod to us and the mention of 'our welcome guests', and then there was singing, loud and joyous, triumphant almost, as if the female soloist, backed by the small choir, was both acknowledging and transcending the history that lay in her past. After all our quiet meditations, it was nice to be part of a different type of worship: boisterous, Christian, public.

The good reverend's sermon, delivered in the same proud, happy voice we'd heard at the inn, blended with the kinds of things I'd been musing on as we'd made the short drive that morning: "Jesus loves you just exactly the same," he said, "no matter what you do. No matter if you're rich or poor, if you work at some important job in a suit, or toil away in greasy or paint-spattered work clothes, if you're nice-looking or maybe not as nice-looking, if you're heavy or light, black or white, or anything in between." He gestured again to Rinpoche, sitting beside me in the middle of the back row. "We have in our midst today a man of the cloth, a holy man of a different faith, someone the Good Lord arranged for me to meet on my recent brief vacation. Jesus loves him, too, though he doesn't wear the cross around his neck. Our guest was wise enough to point out to me, during our breakfast together in North Carolina, that we ought to try to love each other with the purity of dogs and horses. Those creatures ask for very little, don't they? To be fed and housed. And, in return, look what they give us: an abundant love, free of opinion and judgment, a Jesus-like love that sees not our clothes, bodies, or occupations. A love that never, ever, wavers. The point, my brothers and sisters, is that our challenge on this terrible, beautiful earth is to toss aside from our lives anything that gets in the way of that love. Any kind of cheating, any kind of harming of another human being, any kind of behavior the Good Book would frown upon. All of that is like a heavy cloth hanging over our heads, covering our eyes and faces, and it goes by the name of 'sin'. Sin blinds us to the love of Jesus, which is why that love is often referred to as His *light*. We're all sinners, some more so than others. And so we all have our spiritual work to accomplish in this life, that work being the thinning out of that heavy cloth. Eventually, we'll hope to remove it completely. On that day, our faces uncovered, our vision untroubled, our differences reduced to nothing, the light of Jesus's love will shine upon us and give us the eternal rest for which we've been toiling on this blessed earth."

This sermon was punctuated periodically by "Amen!" shouted out from different parts of the nave. The congregants were mostly old, carefully dressed, but not in a way that suggested wealth. Here and there I could see a teenager or young child, but the average age must have been in the sixties, and I couldn't help but wonder how the Bethel would survive in the near future. When the time came to put a donation into an envelope and hand it to a woman carrying a cotton sack, I gave everything that remained in my wallet and pocket, carrying on, as I did so, a silent interior argument with Natasha's cynical ex, Laurence. 'I have enough, I have too much', I was saying to him. There were million-dollar second homes on golf courses just up the road, the word 'plantation' still in their titles. From this pew, I was going to head out to what I expected would be a very pleasant house on a beautiful beach, and probably a fine dinner, as well. Only a Laurence could say there was something wrong with making a large donation. Only the skewed thinking of the skewed modern American era could turn a simple act of generosity into something evil.

The service went on for a long while, with more singing and Bible readings, and when it finally concluded, Reverend Harrelson stood outside on the front walk and greeted and thanked people by name. When Rinpoche approached, the Reverend's cheeks bunched up to either side of the top of his mask. "I knew you'd come, my brother," he said. "Somehow I knew you would."

Rinpoche said nothing, only pressed his palms together and bowed deeply from the waist. The Reverend laughed happily and shook my hand, and, as we walked away, an elderly couple getting into their Oldsmobile called out, "We thank you for coming. Hope to see you again." And that was all. I'd read somewhere that the A.M.E. congregation a few miles down the road, the place where the crazy young white man had slaughtered the people he'd prayed with, had run a service of forgiveness for him. And I wondered how many other congregations would be capable of doing that.

Rinpoche drove, and all the way up Highway 17, riding through echoes of a sordid history, I thought about the Henley lyrics I'd heard in the Island Cafe, what he called 'the heart of the matter.'

Thirty-One

Even with the help of the satellites, it took a while to find the house Anthony had rented for us. We wandered around the grid of roads behind Litchfield Beach, the houses there raised fifteen feet on posts, as if demonstrating their respect for the power of the coastal storms that periodically devastated that beautiful part of the world. Back and forth and around and around we drove until, at last, at the end of a dead-end road, having figured out that the actual street address was a little different than what Chantelle had sent us, we found the house and turned into a driveway paved with pieces of seashell. I'd expected a medium-sized bungalow, perhaps within walking distance of the shore, but even from the back I could tell that the house was more like a small mansion, and right on the beach, a lime green work of art with both an open and glassed-in porch, a turret, and enough windows to suggest a dozen bedrooms. Too luxurious, yes, even a little embarrassing, but it was, I knew, Anthony's way of making up for not spending time with us, and I appreciated that. Still, I fretted that it would feel a little odd, sharing such a huge space with one other person.

I needn't have worried. We'd just stepped out of the truck and grabbed our luggage when I heard the lovely voice of my daughter calling out the beautiful word, "Dad!"

Natasha came trotting down the stairs from the back deck and wrapped me in an embrace to cure every imaginable ill.

"We're all here," she said. "I mean Aunt Seese and Shelsa and me!"

Rinpoche held her in a bear hug, then lifted her into the air with one arm. Another minute and we were up on the deck, greeting my sister and niece. With her long dark hair and dark eyes, Shelsa looked older than her sixteen years, fully grown up. She kissed me daintily on both cheeks and took my hands and kissed them as well, and then she fairly leapt into her father's arms. Greeting my sister, I thought I sensed something in her face and voice—some small trouble of the kind that siblings can feel in each other's presence. But then we were sitting in the kitchen, Shelsa drinking tea, the rest of us drinking coffee, and Natasha was going on, somewhat nervously I thought, about the magnificent house her brother had rented, the gorgeous strand of sandy beach on the other side—"We'll have to take a walk, Dad! You and Uncle Volya will have to take two of the upstairs bedrooms with the views! There's, like, eight of them!"

Shelsa was mostly silent, swinging her baleful eyes from speaker to speaker, sitting close to her father and keeping one hand on his arm at all times. They'd flown from Bismarck to Wilmington, then taken a small plane to Myrtle Beach, and an Uber to the house. And they'd made a shopping trip en route, and had rolls, tuna fish, and cheese, with yogurt and fruit and chia seeds for dessert, and we all got to work and made lunch. It was a little too windy to eat out on the front porch, but I had a chance to survey the view from there: miles of white sand, a short line of posh homes to our right—south. Saltmarsh to the north. "Lunch is on the table, Dad," Tasha said, standing with the door half-open. "What a place Anthony found, right?"

"Incredible," I said. And then, because, again, I sensed something slightly amiss, I added, "Everything good?"

"Good as can be," she said, "on this plane of existence."

Plane of existence was a phrase that had infiltrated our family dialogue over the past decade. Rinpoche used it often in his books, and occasionally in his talks. Seese said it constantly. On that day at least, coming from my daughter, I found it vaguely discomfiting.

My slight sense of unease persisted, even as we sat around the oval dining room table, eating tuna fish sandwiches and apple slices, while Rinpoche and I gave the others a report on the high points of our drive. The unease persisted, too, after we'd spooned through the not-too-sugary desserts and cleaned up.

I was grateful when Natasha suggested we take a walk on the sand, just the two of us, because she'd always been what Jeannie called 'our truth-teller'. A stiff wind, salty and sandy, pushed against us as we headed south, so we didn't say much until, after a mile and a half, we agreed to turn around. "How did Anthony seem?" Tasha asked.

"Busy," I said. "Maybe too busy. Otherwise happy."

We walked along in silence for a few steps, and I began to feel that not saying anything more would be a kind of lie.

"I found myself being pretty judgmental of him, Tash," I admitted. "I think, to a certain extent, I've become like one of those new converts to Christianity who talks about Jesus constantly and wants everyone to reap the benefits of conversion to the One True Faith. Except in my case it's meditation and the examined life."

"I don't get that from you, Dad."

"Thanks. I mean, interiorly. Meditation, Rinpoche's lessons—it's all changed my life. You can probably see it."

"Everybody sees it."

"And so I guess I want that for him, too. Which is unfair.

He has his own path to tread. Rinpoche told me as much, in his own, kind way."

Natasha was quiet again for thirty or forty steps, the wind at our back now, the occasional modest wave breaking and bubbling in a line of white froth to our right. I decided I'd said enough, and told myself I'd just let her have a chance, but when she didn't speak for several minutes, I said, "I feel like something's going on. Is something's wrong?"

No response. I looked at my daughter, but she had her face turned out to sea.

"Everything all right in Dickinson? Are you unhappy there? Is the meditation center doing well? You and Warren okay?"

"We're fine. There are only a couple of people there right now, doing solitaries, and he and his sister are watching over the place and cooking the meals while we're away."

"I was surprised to see you all here."

"Yeah," a long pause, and then, "Seese and Shelsa are having premonitions. That's why we decided to come, instead of letting you guys travel alone. We were thinking of it even before Seese talked with Anthony, but once she heard about the house he rented, she took it as a sign. It matched her dreams, she said. A big house on the beach."

"What kind of premonitions?"

"That Uncle is sick."

"Rinp? Are you joking?"

"I wouldn't joke about that, Dad."

"Right, sorry. I know you wouldn't. I just . . . he seems the same to me, perfectly fine, lots of energy, sharp as ever."

"Yeah, I was watching him at lunch. The same. But, they're pretty sure."

I felt as though a professional wrestler had slapped me in the back of the head. "I think I would have seen something," I said. "Noticed something. He stumbled once, but he laughed about it and wasn't hurt. We've been together constantly for a week now, I—"

"Yeah, maybe it's just Aunt Seese being anxious."

"Since when is she anxious? She was the least anxious kid I ever saw, and, as an adult, 'anxious' would be the last word I'd ever apply to her."

"Yeah, Dad. She was working the beads all during the flights, though."

"Not so unusual."

"She asked me not to talk about it with you, so I feel a little guilty. She thought you'd think she was just loopy. That was the word she used, 'Your father will think I'm loopy, like he did before we went to Italy'."

"I'm paying for old sins, I guess. I used to think that about her pretty much regularly . . . until I got to know Rinpoche."

"And now?"

"And now, after the Italian trip especially, I understand that she's eminently not loopy. . . . But I admit to falling back on old opinions once in a while when she says or does something so out of the ordinary that it reawakens the old stuff. It was embarrassing sometimes when we were kids. She used to say she remembered the moment of being born, remembered what it was like in 'the other dimension'. Kids in school would give her a hard time about it. I had a wrestling match with one of the wise guys once."

"I can't picture you wrestling, Dad."

"In the dirt, no less. Johnny Mastermann was his name. He'd been taunting Seese mercilessly for weeks. I won, too. I was six-and-one as a young wrestler, and then we graduated to bare knuckle brawling, and I didn't do so well."

"Did Mom know?"

"Mom knew everything. All my embarrassing history."

"And you knew hers?"

"Sure, but not much of it was embarrassing. Her family liked to say they were 'comfortable'. 'Privileged' would be the word for it now."

"Like us."

"Yes, like you. Like us. No question. This whole trip was about trying to share some of that. Only I have other roots, as you know, so the word—the economic sense of that word—feels like it fits only part of my life, not the North Dakota part. If someone had used that word with my parents, who worked like a pair draft horses and didn't have much, they would have been furious. And Mom and I weren't exactly gushing with money for the first years we were together."

"It's not just about money, Dad."

"I know that."

Another pause. The wind was raising sand eddies in front of us, gritty swirls marking invisible gusts, as if the complexities of our conversation, of the modern American conversation, were appearing and disappearing there on the beautiful beach in ephemeral sculptures.

"I just really hope Aunt Seese is wrong this time," Tasha said.

"I think she's wrong. I'd tell you if I'd seen any evidence."

Tasha reached across the short space between us and hooked my right arm with her left for a few steps, and I felt, briefly, that I'd stepped back into an old role: Dad the comforter, telling his worried children that everything would be fine.

Thirty-Two

Seese had researched dinner options—she'd become a master of such things—and told us she'd found a seafood place with great reviews. She made a reservation, on the early side, and at five p.m., we all squeezed into the truck, Rinpoche proudly behind the wheel, and headed off to an establishment called The Hanser House on Route 17, five miles to our north. Inside, we found a bar and various rooms holding four or five tables each. There were framed photos of crabs and shells on the walls, and several others that showed a woman—the restaurant's original owner, we were told—proudly holding up the large fish she'd caught. We were seated at a corner table in a room not far from the bar, and treated to one of the finest seafood meals I've ever eaten: scallops grilled with a little soy sauce, delectably buttery yellow grits, perfect coleslaw, with fried hush puppies as an appetizer, and all the iced tea you could drink.

Mindful of the conversation on the beach, I ate with one eye on the robed man sitting diagonally across from me, bracketed by Seese and Shelsa. Rinpoche looked the way he always looked: happy, grateful for the food, buried in the moment. I watched my sister, too. She was talking perhaps a little more than was customary for her: "It turned out the Camry had some kind of trouble with the transmission. They fixed it in a few hours. Four hundred and ten dollars."

"I'll reimburse you," I said.

She shook her head. "The people at the garage were *so* nice. They said you must have taken good care of the car, Otto, because the valves or something were in good shape, the oil was very clean, and even the tires had a lot more miles on them before you'll need new ones."

"You must have driven pretty fast to get to North Dakota, with a stop for repairs."

"She speeds now, Dad. She's worse than Mom used to be. We got stopped once, by the Minnesota Highway Patrol."

"You don't have to give a blow-by-blow, Tash. Your dad will never trust me again."

Tasha grinned at her and went on, doing her best imitation. "Aunt Seese charmed him. "Lady," he said, "you know you were going eighty-two, correct?"

"'Officer, I'm profoundly sorry,' she said, and she gave him the biggest, saddest smile."

"Profoundly, eh?" the trooper said.

"Deeply."

"He handed back the license and registration and said, 'You're profoundly lucky. Don't go that fast again.'"

"And he let us go."

"I was doing *tonglen* for him while he was checking on his computer to see if I had any record of being stopped. Which I don't, Otto, in case you're wondering."

"I wasn't. Rinp did a nice job on the way south. He drove in Boston, New York, D.C."

"Little bad minutes in the parking garage," Rinpoche admitted.

"Those garages can be awful, Unc," Tasha said, "Everybody has trouble in them."

"Maybe I have a little more trouble than everybody. Man said the bad word to us."

The conversation rolled smoothly along like that, imbued with the sweetness of family love. It was only from Shelsa that

I sensed something might be amiss. She'd learned to speak so early, and then, once she was out of elementary school, seemed to have lost much of her interest in speaking. At the Hanswer House she was listening carefully—you could see that—turning her eyes from one person to the next, smiling, laughing, making a sad face, depending on the subject. But she was almost totally silent. She ate quietly and sat pressed close against her father, as a younger girl might have done. I tried to draw her out. "What have you been up to, Shels?"

She looked at me and the edges of her lips turned up. "I love the farm now more than ever, Uncle Ott. I never want to leave."

"Even in winter?"

"Especially in winter. I love the snow, the sound of the wind, the way ice forms on the edges of the roof of the barn and on the wires. I've been studying Tibetan, too."

"Speak wery good, my daughter. Wery good! Knew it from the past life."

"Have you heard from your Italian friend? Tomasso?"

A smile bloomed, as if I'd asked about a fiancé. "He and his mom are coming to visit us this summer. No threats for a while now, so they think it's safe. We're going to lead a two-week retreat together, she and I. Vegetarian meals. Yoga. Five meditation sessions a day. Walks. A little work in the fields. It's already full!"

"I'm not surprised."

"You'll be there to help us."

"Sure, yes," I said. "I'll wash the dishes and ferry people to and from the bus station. I'll show Tomasso how to play catch. I'll explain the rules of baseball."

"No, no, Uncle, you'll teach!"

"Ha! I'm a good dishwasher, Shels. A good driver, a good

243

snow shoveler and weed puller. I'm not even close to being qualified to teach in a meditation retreat. That's your dad's job."

"You the new teacher now, Otto," Rinpoche said, in a tone that was almost blunt. I looked at him, surprised. He wasn't smiling.

"Humility is a great gift in a teacher," Seese put in kindly.

Natasha leaned against me for a few seconds, a lean of encouragement.

"I eat too much to be a good teacher," I said, trying for a joke, because the odd feeling was back—almost, but not quite, a premonition. The waitress had left the small bowl of hush puppies on the table. I popped one in my mouth. "I worry about not throwing the hatchet well. I get . . . discouraged at moments. I—"

"Ram Dass never claimed to be anything but an ordinary human being, and look at the impact he had!" Seese said. "I saw him once in New Jersey. What a funny man!"

"Dad can be funny," Natasha put in. "You used to be so funny Dad, when we were growing up."

"Goofy, was more like it."

"Cynthia and I want you to do one session a day," Shelsa said, fixing me with those eyes and sweeping straight past my self-effacing denials. "We want you to talk about the meditative life for householders."

Householder, I knew, was a word from Buddha's talks, basically code for 'ordinary person', i.e., someone who wasn't pursuing the monastic life. Shelsa pronounced the word with so much quiet conviction, so much love, so much confidence in my nonexistent abilities, that I laughed. I was sure she wasn't serious and was just trying to flatter me, and, while I appreciated the flattery, I knew I wouldn't be sitting up at the front of one of the retreat rooms giving advice, no matter how appropriately ordinary my resume. That kind of instruction was for the enlightened ones—Rinpoche, Shelsa—and the non-enlightened ones like Ram Dass, Harvard professor-turned-author, who'd at least gone to India and sat at the feet of a guru and meditated for sixteen hours at a time. I'd be there to facilitate, run errands and so on. Which was perfectly fine with me.

"We'll talk," I said. For whatever reason—maybe the creeping anxiety I was beginning to feel then—I grossly overdid on dessert, even though we'd had dessert at the beach house, sharing not one, but two slices of pecan pie with Rinpoche, as the women looked on, amused. "Sharing," in this example, means I had seven bites to his one. I gobbled; he reached across the table and took a polite forkful, and I could tell, I could *sense,* that he was trying to sweep that anxiety away, trying to tell me, wordlessly, that it was okay to indulge once in a while, okay to be goofy, okay to offer a bit of advice here and there, at a retreat talk, say, despite one's imperfections; that whatever happened in this life was part of some unimaginably enormous and mysteriously complicated dance of energy, that the whole point of being alive was to align yourself with that energy, to play your role, hopefully, fearlessly, with as much love and care as you could summon.

When our server stopped by, I grabbed the check, paid with the magical plastic card, and left her a tip equal to the total bill.

Squeezed into the pickup on the way back to the beach, we lavished compliments on the meal, and on what we'd started to call "Anthony's house."

"Wery wery spiritual place, that house," Rinpoche said of the latter. I wondered who the owners were, and what they'd think if they heard one of their renters say those words.

Thirty-Three

When we arrived back at Anthony's House, we went our separate ways. Seese and Rinpoche disappeared upstairs for some alone time. Shelsa brewed a pot of tea and sat at the kitchen table, sipping from a white mug. I caught a glimpse of Tasha, sitting in meditation on a leather sofa in a small side-room lined with shelves of books.

A bit uneasy still, I walked over to the back door—the beachside door—and stepped out onto the large deck. It had been an unusually warm day, the first hints of South Carolina summer already in the air, and the night was nearly as mild as May in New York. We'd eaten early, the sun had just set, and a full moon was hoisting itself free of the dark horizon. The moon cast a wide band of light across the water, as if pointing to the house Anthony had rented for us, as if saying: *look at this; look at your son trying to show his love for you and the rest of the family.* I'd been standing there only a moment when my eyes adjusted to the eerie light, and I realized there were people on the sand nearby, some standing, some sitting on chairs, or cross-legged on blankets. All of them were facing the deck on which I stood. I took three steps farther away from the door and saw that the gathering numbered about two dozen, and that every face was lifted toward me, expectantly it seemed. "What's going on?" I almost said, before I realized that somehow, either via a mysterious telepathy, an announcement on a local alternative radio station, or something Seese or Tasha had posted on social media, the assembled souls—now being joined by others who came walking along the beach, singly and in small groups—had learned that Volya Rinpoche was in the house behind me. I stood there awkwardly for a long minute. No one said anything. I could feel that they all wanted *me* to say something, but I hadn't the slightest idea what I might say, so I turned and went back inside.

My sister had come downstairs and was in the kitchen with her daughter, sipping from a cup of tea in a way that seemed oddly preoccupied, as if she was carrying a great weight on her thoughts.

"Seese," I said, and she turned quickly and offered a wobbly smile. "There's a bunch of people out on the sand, right near the deck."

She appeared unsurprised.

"What's going on?"

"They're waiting for Rinpoche to say a few words, Otto. I'll go upstairs and let him know."

I felt another spasm of annoyance. I stopped myself from saying: *If they seem to just know he's here, why doesn't he just know they're here?!* The appearance of the group on the beach had served only to further unnerve me. Those people—strangers—were apparently tuned to some wavelength that was beyond my capacity to hear . . . and he was *my* brother-in-law. I was his first student. Privileged. Special. Seese's lack of surprise made me feel as though everyone of any spiritual attainment knew something I did not know about the events of the day. An old, old echo of *left-out* rattled around in my brain. I felt like the new kid in school who hadn't been told about the birthday party. Foolish, yes. Petty.

Also true.

Thankfully, by the time I heard footsteps on the interior stairs, I had managed to let the feeling float away.

"Little talk now, Otto," Rinpoche said, turning me with an arm around my shoulders and walking with me as far as the door. He stopped and gestured forward with his free arm. "You go," he said. "Tell them thank you. Say them that I have to pee—I'm the old man now—then coming out to say to them hello!" He began laughing, a giggly riff, as if the fact that he had to empty his bladder before the talk was the greatest of The Great Spirit's jokes.

I stepped outside. In my brief absence the crowd had doubled. Fifty people now, with fresh arrivals setting up beach chairs at the back. I walked over to the top step and cleared my throat. "Uh, Rinpoche's here," I said, as if they didn't already know that. "He has to . . . he said to tell you he has to pee, and then he'll be right out."

A smattering of laughter. The splash and *pssh* of surf in the distance. Moonlight on the beach. I turned to head back inside, but ended up opening the door for Rinpoche, who touched my arm in thanks and strode out to the edge of the deck. Not knowing what else to do, I followed and stood off to the side as unobtrusively as possible. People in the group began applauding and calling out greetings: "We love you, Rinpoche!" "Thank you, Rinpoche!" I saw him raise both hands, palms forward, a humble gesture of greeting, then he took a seat on the top step and arranged his robe between and around his knees. The group fell silent. He gestured for me to come and sit among them, and as I went down the stairs, a youngish man stood up out of his chair, and I took it gladly.

"Good that you came here," Rinpoche began. "Nobody is too cold?"

A chorus of "No!" I had a sweater on and could feel a sea breeze brushing the back of my neck, but there was no northern chill in the air.

"Just a small talking now," Rinpoche said. "You hear me okay?"

Another chorus, "Yes!"

"Good. This night wery beautiful. Listen the sound the big ocean make." He paused. "Look at the light from the moon." Another pause. "Feel the winds, little bit of sand in it. Nice, beautiful, yes?"

"Yes!!"

Rinpoche ran his eyes left to right over the assembly, which, I could sense, was still growing behind me. "I made a trip this week with my brother-and-waw," he pointed to me. "Otto. My brother-and-waw. Wery good man! Soon the famous teacher!"

An embarrassing and mercifully brief ripple of applause.

"I am married with his good sister," Rinpoche said, nodding somberly. "Good karma for me!" More applause. "We take a drive from Boston to here this week, Otto and me, wery nice. But everywhere we go we feel sadness, yes? Sadness about the terrible war. You can imagine about the things happening there, the pain some people have, their mothers and brothers dying, the soldiers and the other people having the terrible wombs, losing their houses, the different kind of bad noises there, the different kinds of smells, the different kinds of things you see. All the kinds of suffering." He drew a breath and slowly exhaled. "And when we were on the trip, we see people and feel other sadnesses. A woman lost her house and her husband from Syria. Homeless man wrapped up like this," he pulled the top of his robe up around his neck and cheeks. "Children with the bad diseases that my good brother-and-waw give money

---

for. One friend we talk to who lose his father and mother because of the Hollowcost from another war. Then the food pan tree for the people who have not enough food now, here, in America. Many things like this, many sadnesses we feel on this trip driving here."

Rinpoche reached up and ran his fingers and palms along the length of both cheeks, letting the littlest fingers drag across his lips, almost as if he were drawing lines of tears on his skin. "And I am thinking, maybe everybody is thinking: why this happen? How can this be? How can the evil man start a wars? How can children get so sick? How can the pamdemic kill so many people when the people who love them can't go in the hospital to be with them? Why life is like this?" He let the question hang in the air for a moment. "I don't know an answer," he said, shaking his head at his own ignorance. "Nobody knows it." For a few seconds, as he shifted his weight from hip to hip and rearranged the robe beneath his ample posterior, I thought Rinpoche would end his talk there and leave the listeners half-buried in the awfulness of life, without hope or explanation.

"But," he said, and I could feel the relief in my own body and in the salty air around me. "I don't know, but maybe Buddha is right when he say, "life is suffering". Not *only* suffering. We're not suffering now, probably, all of us on this sand, near this water, all the people in these beautiful houses," he swung an arm to his right to encompass the string of beachfront homes. "We had a little while ago a wery delicious dinner with a big desserts and we weren't suffering. . . . But maybe we suffered before, and maybe we will suffer between now and the when we die. Probably we will. But why is? Makes me wery sad some days to think about this. All over the world, to think about the people hungry, or in the war, or sick. I many times think about this." Behind me I could hear someone quietly crying. Rinpoche seemed to hear it, too. He looked in the direction of the sound, and the sadness there seemed for a moment to be reflected on his features. "Maybe," he said, "the bad people, the Putin, are new to being here on this earth. First life as a human person, maybe, for him. He doesn't feel for other people, so he can hurt them. He think only about himself. Wery bad karma! Maybe now he has many many many more lifes to suffer in, to learn not to hurt. Maybe some wery good people suffer now because they want to take the suffering from someone else, or finish with their karma and not be reborn," he looked at me. "Reborn, yes?"

I nodded.

"Maybe this pain, this suffering, is the number one hardest wesson for us. Maybe for the best people the pain tells us: go away now, don't come back into a body never again. Go on the different level, not this earth, not in this place of suffering. Don't grasp for another time here, more sex, more eating, more money, more big houses, beautiful face, beautiful body, famous. Let go, let go. Maybe the pain pushes us so we let go easier, don't want to come back. I don't know this, but maybe."

He looked down at his hands for a long time, a full minute, at least. Behind and around me I could feel an absolute stillness. The crying had ceased. Only the sound of the muted surf filled the air. That and a sense of expectancy, as if now the answer to all our earthly misery was about to be revealed.

Rinpoche looked up. "Wery easy to say this," he said. "But when you suffering, wery hard. When you are dying, can be wery hard, for you or for the people who loves you. Wery real and no words can make it softer sometimes. . . . You can't all the time be thinking about suffering, all the time be worrying. But you can remember about it little bit in your mind. When you sit to meditate, you remember. You don't hold on too strong to the sex, to the food, to the things you have, the house, the new truck, the thinking about taking a travel. Enjoy, yes, but don't hold too strong! No grasping to it! Then you go quiet in the mind. Maybe not the first time you try meditation, maybe not the first year or twenty year. But soon you go quiet inside. You maybe touch the quietness, the divine quietness—yes, Otto?"

I nodded a second time.

"The divine quietness!" he repeated happily, as if he'd just thought of the phrase and found it fitting. "Not the dead quietness, but the alive quietness, yes? Make you are happy when you touch that, yes? *That* happiness you hold onto, strong, and then, after you die, you see where it brings you, okay?"

"Okay!" a few people responded.

Another deep breath, the famous smile. "No questions this time, okay? Just, if you want, come up and I giving you the hug. I giving you the blessing, and you giving it to me, same time. Like we are connected inside. Like making the love but not the sex, see? We are alive together in the divine quiet, see?"

"Yes!" someone shouted from behind me. "Thank you, Rinpoche!!"

There were a few more thank-yous. Someone directly behind me called out, "More, Rinpoche! More, please!" but Rinp was shaking his head in very small movements. He stood and stepped onto the sand, and people crowded around him, hugging and being hugged, saying a few words, lifting their babies and small children into the air so he could touch them. I stepped aside and watched and did not feel left out at all then, but exactly the opposite: I felt that, over the years of our acquaintance, Rinpoche had let me in on a marvelous secret, but, at the same time, I imagined I could hear the voices of my more cynical New York colleagues, mocking voices. The hugging, the words, the mixed-up grammar and faulty pronunciation, the children held up for a touch from the great man— certain smart people in my circle of acquaintance would have nothing but mockery for all of it. *Life can be brutal,* they would say, *we agree.* But, like Mike at The Morehead Inn, they'd believe that life's brutality was simply the random play of a merciless non-God. Their answer to suffering would be *carpe diem.*

That belief system, I suppose, was as legitimate a response to the human condition as was the one Rinpoche had just offered. Hopelessness versus hope. The hard immediacy of this tortured *now,* versus something my acquaintances would call a fantasy, wishful thinking, nothing divine about it.

But, clumsy and flawed man that I was, in my years of meditation I had touched, however briefly and sporadically, the divine quiet Rinpoche had just described. Strange as it may seem, I had sensed it, too, in Jeannie's final moments, as the horror of her pain seemed finally to release her, and she was gliding away from us. I had sensed something then. *An understanding,* Tasha had called it as we walked down the hill from Agnese's house near Lake Como. I saw that understanding in Jeannie's features, so drawn and withered by the disease. No one, and no intellectual argument, would ever convince me that what I had tasted in meditation and seen on my wife's face in those last moments wasn't real. Where it led, if it led anywhere, I didn't know, but it seemed to me to give the lie to Mike and his cynical *carpe diem,* to undercut the mockery, the worship of one's own intellect, the faith in nothing but randomness. Rinpoche's presence seemed to give the lie to it, too, and I stood and watched for a full hour as the man who'd married my sister stood there in the sand, blessing and being blessed by the believers who'd come down to Litchfield Beach in South Carolina to hear him give his 'little talk'.

Thirty-Four

The crowd very slowly dispersed. I had climbed back onto the deck and was starting toward the door when Rinpoche touched me on the arm and said, "We sit outside now, you and me, Otto." From one of the pockets of his robe he took the two cigars Anthony had given us, then a box of matches. "We gonna make a little smoke!"

"Sure, okay, Rinp," I said, because, mildly surprised as I was by the invitation, at that point I would have done pretty much anything my brother-in-law suggested. There were times when I felt a great force emanating from him, a certainty, and that was one of those times.

We pulled two of the comfortable, all-weather chairs close to each other on the ample deck, and Rinpoche lit both cigars, one after the next, as if he'd been using tobacco since grade school in Skovorodino. We sat half-turned toward each other, watching the moon make its glorious ascent. I felt a peculiar exaltation then, a small, happy roiling in the middle of my upper body. We puffed away like men who'd just won an NBA championship. It was the seventh game of the finals. We'd been playing the Celtics, who'd been big favorites at the start of the series. The massive crowd was electric, everyone on their feet, screaming, weeping, praying. With two seconds remaining, I'd sent Rinpoche a no-look pass between the legs of a six-foot-ten defender, and Rinp had taken one step and lifted himself magically up and up and slammed the ball through the basket with one hand, bending the rim down just as the buzzer sounded and the outline of the glass backboard went red.

An odd mood, it was, the anxiety momentarily gone, the future expansive, the possibilities endless. For that little while, as we sent out plumes of sweet smoke, it seemed to me that all the world's suffering must eventually lead toward something other than despair and death and nothingness. I'd listened to so many of Rinpoche's talks, and had read and re-read all his books, but I'd never felt quite as . . . *inspired* is the word, I guess. Uplifted. At peace.

From the center of that mood, these words appeared, and I have thought about them often since then: "Rinp, a question."

"Shoot me."

"How does a person get to really love himself?"

"What you mean? Everybody loves himself, Otto."

"Not really. *I* don't, for example, not completely, not always. And I'm sure I'm not alone. I see now why I was so upset when we were throwing the hatchets. It was like my inability to make the hatchet stick was confirmation of . . . of, I don't know, some kind of general failure. I feel that way after a not-so-good meditation, even though you've told me many times not to. I think, at some level, that I've always felt it, like there's a critical voice running beneath my thoughts and all it takes is a half-hour at the hatchet place, a wrong turn on the road, a bad tennis game or a stupid comment, to turn up the volume. I know people who feel that way all the time, because they don't like their face, their body, their marriage, their kids, or because they're not rich, or famous, or . . . I don't know. I think sometimes that it's an epidemic."

Rinpoche was quiet, looking out to sea. He took a pull on the cigar, held the smoke in his mouth for a few seconds, then—why would I be surprised—blew a perfect ring into the air. Something he'd learned from Les Ingler, perhaps. I thought Rinpoche might laugh at that: both of us watched the ring wobble away and dissipate, but he seemed too pensive to laugh.

I waited.

At last he turned to me and said, "You asked one time on this trip about my mother, remember?"

"Yes."

A grunt, another puff, another smoke ring. I could see that he was concentrating, looking for the best way to answer my question. "Lots of time in this world the men wery important. The Dalai Lama. The Pope. Other men. The resiples around Jesus, yes?"

"Disciples, yes."

"They have the kind of important you can see. My father had it. But my mother had the other kind, the one you can't see." He paused, half-lost in time, searching for the good words. "My father gave me the meditation secrets, the root power I was talking you about. But my mother, she makes me feel in this world that I am part of it. I belong to it, yes?"

"Yes."

"Like the tree, the beach, the moon. Supposed to be here. Like my spirit is the same important part of this world as the dirt that grows food, the rain, the light, see?"

"More or less."

"Shelsa in the talk in Italy that time, she said the meditation is not like a competition, remember? Who is better. Meditation supposed to help you feel you *belong,* you are good. Not *better,* just good. See?"

"I do see. But you and Shels started out with that kind of mother. I didn't. Mom wasn't bad to us, just . . . reserved, almost cold. But I guess I can't blame her for my troubles because Seese had the same mother, and she feels perfectly comfortable with herself. To be totally honest, I do not. I really saw that on this trip so far. The conversation at dinner tonight kind of underlined that."

He sighed, tapped the ash of the cigar onto the deck then rubbed his sandal over it. He looked at me. "Seese make it for herself, that love. So then she can give it to the other people."

"Okay, but *how*, is my question. Therapy? Past-life studies? Penance? Fasting?"

A smile, a lift of the eyebrows. "I give you a new meditation, okay? Every morning and every night you do it. Wery easy one. Three time you say: Big Spirit loves me. Three time you say: People love me. Three time you say: I'm a good person. Okay?"

"Seems a little simplistic," I said, though I regretted the words instantly, and added, "no offense."

He laughed then, a few happy notes. He wobbled the last of the cigar in his fingers and took another drag. "See what happens to the bad voice if you do it every day," he said. "Look who loves you! Anthony, Natasha, Shelsa, my good wife, me, so many people love you. Look how Jeannie, she loved you! Try with that meditation, and maybe pretty soon, you feel it inside you all the times."

"Something about the way we live makes it hard to feel. For me, anyway."

"Inside the big world, you make a small one, Otto. Inside that small world, there's the quiet. Inside that quiet, you gonna feel this love all the time, okay?"

"Okay, thanks."

"You welcome. We take a little walk now, you and me. A stroller. On this special beach."

It had grown darker by then—the moon was well up in the

sky and smaller—and it was fairly late, so I was somewhat surprised at the idea of a walk. What surprised me more was that
Rinpoche didn't go inside and ask Seese, Tasha, and Shelsa to
join us. I had the sense then, another flutter of the earlier intui-
tion, that the three women knew something I didn't, that there
was some plan afoot, and I wasn't being let in on it. I remember looking through the window for a second and seeing Tasha
on the couch, phone in hand, no doubt in mid-communication
with the man Seese liked so much, and I'd met only twice. Warren. I hoped there was no trouble between them. I knew that, if
Natasha had children with him, she'd be the kind of mother
Rinpoche had just described: From the first instant of their
lives, her children would feel that they belonged on this earth,
that they were loved. The thought made me happy.

Rinpoche stood. Down the short flight of sandy wooden
steps we went, tossing the cigars onto the sand and making sure
they were snuffed out. Without saying anything, we stood for a
few seconds at the top of the beach and admired the dark
spread of the ocean, white bands of bright surf bubbling there
for a moment, then gone.

Looking up at the moon, it struck me, not for the first time,
that so much of what we thought we were seeing was actually
an illusion. So much of what we thought we knew came from
the information provided by our senses. But what if that lens—
our senses—was, in fact, less perfect than we believed? What if
our prime flaw was a kind of hubris, a failure to admit the limi-
tations of the human brain? Yes, the study of science had informed us—after we'd been mistaken for countless millennia—
that the moon was not, in fact, rising. It only appeared to rise
because of the rotation of the earth, an incredibly rapid spin
that felt like stillness to us, like nothing at all. Yes, after we'd
been mistaken for countless millennia, we now knew that the

light we called a 'star' was light that had been traveling for thousands upon thousands of years, and that the celestial body from which it had emanated might no longer even exist. My scholarly friends believed humanity would just keep studying and researching and learning, and little by little we'd figure our way through the great volumes of knowledge contained in the universes. We'd find the answers, all of them. Our amazing human brains would lead us, generation by generation, century by century, to the ultimate truth. To a full sense of belonging, perhaps.

But what if we couldn't find the truth that way? What if the universe was expanding, as scientists claimed, and the ultimate answers kept moving away from us faster than our knowledge could increase? What if the idea of God, or the Divine Intelligence, an idea shared by so many humans from the beginning of time, was destined to indicate what we could not ever know? We were specks, after all. Essential, perhaps, in one way, but specks of consciousness in a realm so vast that even the farthest-reaching telescopes couldn't see an endpoint. We were dust. Ash. A bit of flesh and bone with a brain that was figuring and figuring, calculating and planning and strategizing, but on one level utterly helpless, adrift, at the mercy of something so much larger.

Rinpoche and I stood and contemplated the magnificence. I tried, as he'd urged me time and again, to let go of the thinking mind, to move to a place beyond figuring and calculating, beyond words. To feel myself beloved, belonging, in my proper place.

A small shiver went through me. Rinpoche might have noticed, or might have been feeling what I was feeling then, or might have been feeling it always, from long before we'd come to know each other. He reached out and wrapped an arm around my shoulders, then let go, and we angled down toward the water.

The tide was high on that night, the surf gentle, the beach empty, the other houses off-season dark. As we walked toward the water, the moonlight and the quiet lap of the waves seemed to fill me to bursting.

"We have to make a swim," Rinpoche said quietly, almost as if he were speaking to himself.

"Sure," I said. "If it's warm again tomorrow, we can go in. The water didn't seem that cold when I was wading this afternoon."

"Swim now, I mean, Otto."

"Really? In the dark?"

He lifted his robe over his head and spread it on the dry sand. "Put your clothes on top of it here," he said. Off came his sandals, his underwear. I was left with no choice but to strip down on the dark beach, though I have to say that the idea of swimming in a cold, unlit ocean held little appeal.

Naked as the day we were born, Rinpoche and I waded in, stopping for just a few seconds when the water reached our knees. Stopping again after another few steps. And then we were waist-deep—the water very cold, but not unbearably so— and I heard a splash and stood there, watching for Rinpoche to surface. I knew, from other swims, how long he could hold his breath, and when he didn't appear after ten or fifteen seconds, I took the plunge myself. That first violent shock, the Atlantic holding me in its frigid embrace. I kicked and stroked, and by the time I'd traveled a short distance and come up for air, Rinp was surfacing with a spray of breath, a whale with a huge smile on its face. "YAHHH!" He shouted into the night, as happy a sound as I've ever heard. I watched him flip onto his back, and I did the same, a few stars surviving the moon's brightness, the vast black sky, the gentle, unpredictable lift and drop of the sea. For a minute or so, before a deeper chill started to take hold, I felt a rush of the purest joy, of not-caring, not-worrying, not-growing-old.

I started to shiver then, small, watery trembles, and we turned and headed back to shore, stroking and kicking to fend off the chill, Rinp making big, clumsy splashes and gasping for air. On the sand again we did a sort of naked, old-man's trot twenty yards up and down the beach before we pulled our clothes on over still-wet bodies, both of us laughing like kids who'd gotten away with something, who were free.

We heard footsteps, and saw a woman jogging along the sand. She was holding a leash and leading a small white poodle. "Hey guys!" she called as she passed. We greeted her in return and watched her run, the poodle dutifully keeping step.

When we were alone again, Rinpoche said, "Dyin' now, Otto."

I thought he was using part of a phrase, as he was sometimes known to do, that he was trying to say, "Dying to get back to the house now, Otto." Or "Dying to get warm." Or, "Dying to get something to eat." Or, "Dying to spend time with my wife."

But he was quiet then, squeezing me against him, shoulder to shoulder, the clothes damp from our wet skin, and then a thought, one prick of light in a dark sky, appeared. "Who is?" I asked.

"Rinpoche," he said, speaking of himself in the third person, something I hadn't heard him do for quite a while.

"You lost me, Rinp."

He laughed. "Dyin' now. I wanted to tell you this."

I stopped and turned, freeing myself from his arm. In the moonlight, for the first time I could remember, his face looked like the face of an old man. His smile, trembling very slightly, squeezed a whole field of wrinkles up around his cheekbones and eyes. I remembered what Tasha had told me on our walk, and realized that I'd pushed it to the back of my mind.

"You're sick?"

The smile faded slightly. He shook his head, no. "Now only the finish of this life," he said. "Not the same as sick."

"What do you mean, Rinp?" I asked, but at some buried level, I knew exactly what he meant. "When? Why? Of what?"

He shrugged and kept his eyes locked on my eyes. "Now goin' inside the house and dyin'. I wanted to take a last swim with my brother-and-waw that I love."

"I don't understand," I said. But, of course, I did.

He grabbed me then, wrapped me in a tremendous hug and held on for a long few seconds. I was shaking, and it felt like he was trying to squeeze the shakiness out of me, to warm me and plant me more solidly in my rightful place on this earth.

"Seese knows," he said. "They know." He let go and swung an arm toward the house. "I wanted me to tell you, not them to."

"But why? Why now? How do you know?"

"You feel it," he said, and we were walking up the steps.

The women were waiting for us, and now I could see on my daughter's face that she knew what was about to happen, or thought she knew. I clung to the hope that she must be mistaken, that my foolish sister had had one of her 'visions', some message from the other realms, and had convinced Rinpoche that his time was at hand, and then passed that message on to Tasha and Shelsa. For a second then, chilled, skin sticky from the salty swim, I felt so alienated from them, from all of them. They were irrational, knowing someone would die even though he appeared perfectly healthy, vibrant and alive enough to take a cold swim in the South Carolina ocean in March! But then Shelsa took her father by the hand, and something in that gesture was so otherworldly, so gentle and *knowing,* that I started to tremble again. They moved into the larger of the two living rooms. I trailed behind. The women had set up pillows on the floor in a small circle. Rinpoche took off his sandals, sat cross-legged on the largest pillow, and laughed and brushed sand from his bare feet. "What a good last swim we had!" he said, and Natasha started to weep.

I sat beside her, all of us within a few feet of each other. I wanted to put my hand on my daughter and comfort her, but for some reason I couldn't do that. Rinpoche was arranging himself in a comfortable position, little movements I'd seen him make scores of times before he started in on one of his talks. Seese watched him with a terrible intensity. She leaned slightly forward and put a hand on the top of his right knee and Rinpoche covered her hand with his and patted it gently a few times, smiled at her, then looked at all of us in turn. He reached out with his left hand and brushed the side of his daughter's face, moved the hand to the top of Natasha's head—she was crying quietly now. Instead of touching me, he just looked at me, unblinking, five seconds, eight seconds, ten seconds, and the only way I can describe that look is to say that it contained within it an absolute love, pure and clean as the air on a North Dakota summer day. He held me that way, his lips moving at the corners, a smile worthy of the Buddha himself, then he patted and squeezed Seese's hand once more, touched his daughter lightly on top of her right shoulder, said, "Only try." And closed his eyes.

I sat there as if made of stone. I don't know that I was even breathing, or blinking. I could sense Tasha's sadness, but as if from a great distance. I watched Rinpoche, watched him, eyes closed, take three medium-deep breaths, blowing the last one out long and steady between parted lips. And then he was perfectly still, and for one-half of one second I thought I saw what I can only describe as a rainbow around him, a shimmering light of different colors.

And then it was gone. I felt the tears running down my face, and reached out at last and held my daughter's fingers in mine, then I lowered my chin to my chest and let myself weep, because one of the finest spirits ever to walk the earth had left this life, on the night of a full moon, in our presence, in a house my son had rented for him, and was now already moving on to other realms.

Afterword

Twelve days later, after we had cremated my brother-in-law's body and driven, with his ashes, all the way back to the farm in North Dakota, after I'd watched my son and daughter weeping there at the ceremony, after we'd had what Seese called 'a celebratory meal' in the house where we'd both been raised, after I'd given Rinpoche's silver truck to Les Ingler, who seemed utterly baffled by the gift and by Rinpoche's passing. . . . After all that, and after dinner on our third day there, my beautiful niece Shelsa suggested I spend the night alone in one of the meditation cabins we'd built on the property. "I think it would be good, Uncle Ott," she said, and I was not about to disagree. The word for what I felt then was *humbled.* I knew nothing compared to what she and her mother seemed to know. Nothing. They and Tasha were light years ahead of me.

Seese said she'd walk over with me. We pulled on down jackets, hats, and gloves, and stepped outside. It was snowing, and through the whirling flakes, we walked toward the nearest of the three individual-retreat cabins. "Sad?" I asked her, and then felt foolish for asking. Of course she was sad. She'd just lost her husband.

I was starting to apologize, when she said, "A little bit. I'm so lucky, Otto. No one in this big world has been luckier than me."

"I want," I said, and then I had to stop for a moment and

swallow and take a breath. "I feel like he was pointing us in the direction of some other place, some other way."

"Yes."

"I want to go there. Sometimes I feel like I could take one big step and be there. Do you know what I mean?"

"Yes."

"You sensed the existence of that place long before I ever did."

"In my own weird way. I had an inkling, I guess. You were right to call me loopy. I was looping around and around, and then I met Rinpoche, love of my existence, and he showed me a straighter road."

My sister took my arm. The snow was falling harder now, small cold sparks on our cheeks, as familiar to us as the sound of our voices. "So now what, Seese? What do we do now?"

She let out a sad, one-note laugh. "Now we remember," she said, and she hugged me hard, just for a second, and turned and walked back toward the house.

Inside the cabin, I filled and lit the woodstove, then sat in meditation for a time, climbed into the bed, and pulled the blanket and quilt up under my chin. It had been an exhausting series of days, and I soon fell asleep.

Somewhere in the small, dark hours of morning I dreamt of Rinpoche. In the dream he was very much alive, happy, beaming, shining, looking straight into my eyes and about to burst into one of his long riffs of laughter. I was struggling to ask him questions—"Where are you now? How can I find you?"—but the words wouldn't rise up out of my throat, and I was left with a terrible frustration.

I awoke from that dream to the sense of another presence in the room. The hair on my arms was standing at attention, and I was afraid to turn my eyes, so I kept looking straight up at the ceiling. At last, summoning a drop of courage, I managed to squeak out one word, "Rinp?" The sound of my own voice terrified me. There was no answer, of course, but the vivid sense of his presence persisted, and I lay there, feeling that presence, remembering him. It felt undeniably true that I was making a real connection with him, that the part of me that was separate from my body and mind and personality had aligned itself with Rinpoche's spirit, that we were momentarily linked in some other dimension, in the kind of place my sister had talked about for decades, and I had silently mocked. It was just my imagination, some would say. Just a pleasant fantasy, a way of compensating for the loss. Simply the remnants of the dream. But, if anything, those moments felt more real than any other moments in my life. If I 'turned' my mind slightly to one side, I could sense Jeannie's spirit, too, just as vividly. I recalled Seese saying at the Afghani restaurant that, in her hospital bed she'd had a sense of 'all these spirits' close around her. Beyond or beneath that memory, my mind was completely empty and quiet except for this overwhelming certainty—impossible to capture in words—that I remained connected to a similar assembly of spirits, that all of us—Seese and Natasha and Anthony and Shelsa and Jeannie and Rinpoche and I—were linked in the fields of eternity, that we'd been set down together in a certain place, for a certain amount of time, in bodies that were designed to function for a while and then cease functioning, and that there was a very specific, larger purpose to our acquaintance, to our love for each other. It seemed clear to me that Rinpoche had understood all this, and that Shelsa understood it, that they'd been born with that understanding the way Mozart had been born with an understanding of music, and that my small but essential role in the universe was to try and keep trying to grasp what they had always known, the way, after decades of determined practice, a lover of music might, one fine day, play fairly well a piece that Mozart had set down on a page hundreds of years earlier.

There in the dark cabin in the fields of North Dakota, with a wintry wind singing just beyond the walls, that feeling, that hyper-real sense, persisted for several remarkable minutes. And then it passed, and I slept, and awoke hours later to what was for me a completely changed world.

And I have tried my best to live in that world ever since, and to do it justice in these stories.

The End

7 March, 2022, Conway, Massachusetts
24 January, 2023, Rapallo, Italy

Acknowledgments

First thanks, as always, to Amanda, for her love and support. It's not easy being married to a writer—the artistic life is a roller coaster of elation and disappointment—and she is a steady beacon of sanity and generosity. She's also my first reader, a gatekeeper, who has saved me from many navigational errors.

My profound thanks to Alexandra and Juliana, brightest stars in our sky, whose courage, positivity, honesty, and warmth are a continuous inspiration to their old dad.

I'm grateful to my publisher Peter Sarno for his untiring work on my behalf. A novelist himself, Peter knows the challenges involved in trying to capture a slice of life on the page. His wisdom, expertise, and friendship should all be read between the lines of this book.

Robert Braile, another wonderful friend and fine writer, went through this manuscript with his careful editor's eye, made excellent suggestions, identified weak spots, and caught a small boatload of mistakes. He and Peter have been indispensable to my work, and I'm indebted to both of them.

My gratitude to Peggy Moss, John Beebe, Jessica Lipnack, and Peter Wiley for cover consultations (in the end, the decision on which cover to use, as well as any mistakes in the text, belong to me). Beside being great friends, Peggy and Jessica—both magnificent writers—have, for years, been a deep well of encouragement from which I've often drawn.

Lastly, I'm grateful to the many readers of 'The Buddha Books,' especially those who took the time to write me emails and letters, subscribe to *On the Plus Side*, and read the newsletter. You will never know how important those notes and that support have been to me over the sixteen years of this series.

It seems I tend to write books in groups of four: Four Revere novels, four *Buddha* novels, four World War II historical novels. The time has come, I think, to begin the next quartet.

Roland Merullo is an awarding-winning author of 27 books including 20 works of fiction: *Breakfast with Buddha*, a nominee for the International IMPAC Dublin Literary Award, now in its 21st printing; *The Talk-Funny Girl*, a 2012 ALEX Award Winner and named a "Must Read" by the Massachusetts Library Association and the Massachusetts Center for the Book; *Vatican Waltz* named one of the Best Books of 2013 by *Publishers Weekly*; *Lunch with Buddha* selected as one of the Best Books of 2013 by *Kirkus Reviews*; *American Savior*, a Massachusetts Center for the Book, "Honor Award" winner; *In Revere, In Those Days* a Booklist Editors' Choice Recipient; *Revere Beach Boulevard* named one of the "Top 100 Essential Books of New England" by the *Boston Globe*; *A Little Love Story* chosen as one of "Ten Wonderful Romance Novels" by *Good Housekeeping* and *Revere Beach Elegy* winner of the Massachusetts Book Award for nonfiction.

Merullo's essays have appeared in numerous publications including the *New York Times, Yankee Magazine, Newsweek,* the *Boston Globe, the Philadelphia Inquirer, Boston Magazine, Reader's Digest, Good Housekeeping,* and the *Chronicle of Higher Education.* Merullo's books have been translated into German, Spanish, Portuguese, Korean, Croatian, Chinese, Turkish, Slovenian, Bulgarian, Czech, and Italian.

He has been a frequent contributor of commentary for National Public Radio affiliates.

Some Other Books by PFP/AJAR Contemporaries

Waking Slow – **Ioanna Opidee**
"*Waking Slow* shines light on not just the extremes of violence, but the more subtle and insidious indignities and inequalities around us. ...[Ioanna] Opidee has given us a sensitive protagonist who walks the uncomfortable, universal line between alienation and acceptance. The book offers a look at what it takes to put the shards back together after a shattering, showing not that it's easy, or fast, but possible."
—Nina MacLaughlin, ***Boston Globe***

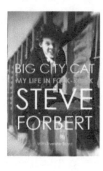

Big City Cat: My Life in Folk Rock
- Steve Forbert
"Like his stunning first album, Steve's compelling first book is very much alive on arrival."
—David Wild,
contributing editor, ***Rolling Stone***

Lunch with Buddha - **Roland Merullo**
"A beautifully written and compelling story about a man's search for meaning that earnestly and accessibly tackles some well-trodden but universal questions. A quiet meditation on life, death, darkness and spirituality, sprinkled with humor, tenderness and stunning landscapes."
—***Kirkus*** –Starred Review / "Best of 2013"

This Is Paradise: An Irish mother's grief, an African village's plight, and the medical clinic that brought fresh hope to both
- **Suzanne Strempek Shea**

—Named to *Yankee Magazines'* 2014 "New England Wish List."

Smedley's Secret Guide to World Literature - **Askold Melnyczuk**
"A teen, wired more to his phone than the repercussions of his actions [who] is trying to make sense of his life. Melnyczuk captures these existential dilemmas in a believable voice." —Clea Simon, *Boston Globe*

Who Do You Think You Are?: Reflections of a Writer's Life
- **Joseph Torra**

"A memoir about one man's life of writing and self-discovery that flows in a natural way and hums with a sense of honesty."
—*Kirkus Reviews*

Visions of Johanna - **Peter Sarno**

"Sarno's beautifully written literary novel concerns an unlikely pairing...The author skillfully portrays Matt, drawing readers into the story with his use of metaphor and lush language...As the story reaches its affecting conclusion, readers may even shed a tear or two."
—*Booklist,* **starred review**

Made in United States
Troutdale, OR
11/24/2023

14873138R00174